BRITISH BUILT AIRCRAFT

VOLUME 4
Central & Eastern England

BRITISH BUILT AIRCRAFT

VOLUME 4
Central & Eastern England

Ron Smith

TEMPUS

First published 2004

Tempus Publishing Ltd
The Mill, Brimscombe Port
Stroud, Gloucestershire GL5 2QG

British Library Cataloguing in Publication Data.
A catalogue record for this book is available from the British Library.

ISBN 0 7524 3162 5

Typesetting and origination by Tempus Publishing.
Printed in Great Britain.

Contents

Introduction

This volume is the fourth in a series of five, which, when completed, will provide a complete record of aircraft construction in Britain. Each volume focuses on a different regional area, documenting activity over the whole period from 1908 until the present day, keyed to the places where this enterprise was actually performed. The objective of the whole work is to pay tribute to the heritage of the British aircraft industry, and to create and preserve a record of its lost endeavours. The preceding volumes covered, respectively, aircraft built in Greater London; South West and Central Southern England; and South East England.

As soon as one starts to examine the history of the aircraft industry, it becomes clear that it has developed through a number of distinct phases. These phases can be characterised as: the pioneers (1908 to 1914); First World War mass production (1914 to 1918); collapse and re-birth between the wars (1919 to 1939); Second World War mass production (1939 to 1945); post-war (1945 to 1960); and modern times. A discussion of the evolution of the industry covering these six main periods of activity can be found in Section One. The aim of this review of the evolution of the industry is to place the remainder of the work within the overall context, while highlighting developments that are specific to the area of Central & Eastern England.

Some twenty-five years ago, on the formation of British Aerospace (BAe), the American magazine *Aviation Week & Space Technology* wryly commented that the final phase of development of the Society of British Aircraft Constructors (SBAC) had now taken place. Whereas previously the numerous members of the SBAC had reflected the vigour, diversity and inventive spirit of the British industry, it had, following restructuring in 1960, been reduced to the 'Society of Both Aircraft Companies' (namely, the British Aircraft Corporation and Hawker Siddeley Aviation Ltd). The formation of BAe was the final act in the process, with the once great industry reduced to the 'Single British Aerospace Company'.

This light-hearted comment contains an important message. British aircraft industry names, which were once well known to the public, have disappeared from the day-to-day business of manufacturing aeroplanes. Indeed, in many instances, their operating sites have even disappeared from the map. At first sight it seems as if the once vibrant British aircraft industry has contracted virtually to the point of extinction since the Second World War. The entire industry has been reduced to the firms of BAE SYSTEMS, AgustaWestland, Slingsby, and Britten-Norman (surviving, as I write, in its latest manifestation: B-N Group), together with sundry microlight and home-built aircraft suppliers.

Many British aircraft manufacturers have disappeared altogether and this has provided the inspiration for this survey of the industry. Central and Eastern England has seen the demise of such company names as Sir W.G. Armstrong Whitworth Aircraft Ltd, Auster Aircraft Ltd, Boulton Paul Aircraft Ltd and Percival Aircraft Ltd/Hunting Percival Aircraft Ltd. Simultaneously, aircraft manufacture has ceased at Ansty, Baginton, Bitteswell, Castle Bromwich, Cowley, Ipswich, Lincoln, Longbridge, Norwich, Peterborough, Rearsby, Whitley Abbey and Wolverhampton. It is particularly notable, in this area, how many companies in the motor industry were once associated with the large-scale manufacture of aircraft. Having pondered on these and the many other closures across the country, the idea grew that an effort should be made to record something of Britain's aircraft construction history and heritage.

The first outcome of this desire to document the past achievements of the British aircraft industry was a successful entry in the 1994 Pooley's International Dawn to Dusk Flying Competition by the author, with his colleague Colin Dodds. The entry, under the title *Lost Names in British Aviation*, consisted of the record of a flight made on a single day (between dawn and dusk) in a 1936 de Havilland Hornet Moth, over sites in Britain where aircraft had once been built, by companies that no longer exist. The research carried out in support of that competition entry has been greatly extended to provide the basis for this record of British achievement, innovation, failure and success.

Content

This series of books records British aircraft manufacture in nearly all its manifestations, in the form of a regional survey of the United Kingdom. The scope of the work is deliberately wide, including as many locations as possible where aircraft have been built, whether by their original designers or by contractors. Exclusions are limited to balloons; the majority of gliders and microlight aircraft; and home-built aircraft of foreign design, unless substantially modified in the form flown in the United Kingdom. In general, only the prototypes of British-designed home-built aircraft are included, rather than every single example of any particular type.

Being centred on the various manufacturing sites, the book allows a wider scope than a mere litany of product histories, allowing additional discussion of people, places and events. As a result, the major players of the industry are recorded alongside the wealth of early activity, light aircraft and one-off designs that provide a rich background to the main scene. Such is the scope of this record that the space allocated to any individual firm is necessarily limited. This mainly has the effect of producing a somewhat condensed view of some of the largest and best-known companies. However, this limitation is, hopefully, compensated for by some of the fascinating but unfamiliar material presented, covering many companies that are likely to be unfamiliar to the reader.

Those interested in the detailed history of the major manufacturers will be able to find many excellent books with which to fill in the detail if they wish. The same cannot be said for companies such as R.J. Everett Engineering, Wm Lawrence & Co. Ltd, Helliwells Ltd, Morgan & Co. Ltd, and a number of other lesser known companies from Central and Eastern England that are included here.

Structure

These introductory remarks are followed by a discussion of the evolution of the aircraft industry, highlighting the activities that characterise each of the main periods identified above, and tailored to the specific region covered by this volume. The contraction through successive mergers that has given rise to the present shape of the industry is presented, together with a family tree of British Aerospace (which contains all of the aircraft heritage of the present BAE SYSTEMS).

The main content of the volume follows in Section Two. Volume Four is a survey of aircraft manufacture in Central and Eastern England, as defined by the following counties: Bedfordshire, Cambridgeshire, Derbyshire, Herefordshire and Worcestershire, Leicestershire, Lincolnshire, Norfolk, Northamptonshire, Nottinghamshire, Oxfordshire, Shropshire, Staffordshire, Suffolk, Warwickshire, and West Midlands. The presentation structure is alphabetical by county, and then alphabetical by location. For most locations, individual manufacturers are then presented alphabetically in sequence.

Where activity at a single site has only involved one firm at any time, or where the evolution of a single major firm has dominated a particular site, the presentation is chronological, rather than alphabetical. Bitteswell is an example of such a variation.

When the series is complete it will provide a comprehensive geographic and product history of aircraft construction in the United Kingdom. I have attempted to cover all sites where aircraft manufacture took place, and to select photographs that provide a balanced mix of example products; locations as they are now; and as they were during their heyday; or combinations of these. A number of the photographs are of the sites as taken from the air during the 1994 Dawn to Dusk competition.

Information Sources and Acknowledgements

A number of major reference sources were used to create this survey of the British aircraft industry. Chief among these were magazines such as *Flight, The Aeroplane,* and *Aeroplane Monthly,* and the following books and publications, which provide particularly useful material across the whole spectrum of the industry: Terence Boughton's excellent *History of the British Light Aeroplane*; A.J. Jackson's *British Civil Aircraft since 1919*; the individual company histories published by Putnam; Ken Ellis' *British Homebuilt Aircraft Since 1920*; R. Dallas Brett's *History of British Aviation 1909-14*; Arthur Ord-Hume's encyclopaedic *British Light Aeroplanes – Their Evolution, Development and Perfection 1920-40*; the equally outstanding *British Aircraft Before The Great War* by Michael H. Goodall and Albert E. Tagg; many editions of *Jane's All the World's Aircraft*; a wide range of test pilot autobiographies; and numerous other sources. A bibliography is provided listing the many reference sources consulted.

In setting out to document the British aircraft industry, I wish to give a flavour of the breadth of the endeavour in terms of the diversity of both products and places used for aircraft manufacture. It is not my intention to provide a definitive record of every aircraft built, nor an encyclopaedia of production quantities. In some cases, I have found the latter aspect clouded with uncertainty. Unless clearly definitive data is available, I have used Bruce Robertson's *British Military Aircraft Serials 1878-1987* as a guide when indicating production quantities. I have not hesitated to highlight areas where conflicting information may be found in readily available references. It is for others to research and clarify these issues.

Particular thanks are due to my colleague Rob Preece for the loan of his original, unbound, copies of *Flight* covering the period 1911 to 1923, and to Liz and Peter Curtis for access to a complete collection of *Aeroplane Monthly* magazines. Thanks are also due to Chris Ilett for the loan of *Flight* magazines from 1929 and 1930. A further acknowledgement must be made to The Royal Aeronautical Society library; not only are their early copies of *The Aeroplane* bound complete with their advertising pages, but here I also found a copy of R. Borlase Matthews' *Aviation Pocket-Book 1919-20* whose Gazetteer of the industry put me on the track of many unfamiliar companies. I am most grateful for the assistance provided by George Jenks (AVRO Heritage Centre) and Barry Abraham (Airfield Research Group).

Acknowledgement is due to those companies still extant (and not today associated with the aircraft industry) who answered my correspondence. Mention must also be made of the information and photographs supped for this series by the following: Ken Ellis; Harry Fraser-Mitchell (Handley Page Association); Fred Ballam (Westland); Chris Hodson (Folland Aircraft Ltd); Olivia Johnston (Bombardier Aerospace, Belfast); Sir Arthur Marshall and Sarah Beavis (Marshall Aerospace plc); Mick Ames (International Auster Club Heritage Group); John Collier (additional Auster material); Geoff Negus (material related to Castle Bromwich and Longbridge); Ray Williams (material related to Sir W.G. Armstrong Whitworth Aircraft Ltd); Mrs Clarke of Lawrence Automotive (photographs of aircraft construction at William Lawrence Ltd); and Del Hoyland (Martin-Baker Aircraft Co. Ltd). I am also grateful to Bob Jenner Hobbs of the Association of Transport Photographers and Historians, who maintains the National Archive of Transport, Travel and Trade (NA3T) for assistance in sourcing images from this archive.

I must further acknowledge the access provided to photographic material by my present employer, BAE SYSTEMS. In making this acknowledgement, I should also stress that all

Hornet Moth G-AELO is seen here at Pocklington prior to the 1994 Dawn to Dusk competition flight by Colin Dodds and the author. (Author)

opinions expressed herein are entirely my own. I also acknowledge the permission received from BAE SYSTEMS plc, which enables me to reproduce a number of advertisements from BAE SYSTEMS legacy companies in this volume. Every effort has been made to provide the correct attribution for the illustrations used. Please inform the publisher should any errors or omissions have been made and these will be rectified at the earliest opportunity.

Finally, as indicated earlier, the research for this book was triggered by the successful entry in the 1994 *Pooley's* International Dawn to Dusk competition. This could not have been made without the support, encouragement, experience and competence of my colleague Colin Dodds, who flew the aircraft, and the generosity of David Wells, who made his aircraft, G-AELO, available for the competition flight.

Not Yet Found (and Imperfect Knowledge Disclaimer)

In a work of this scope, it is inevitable that mistakes and omissions will be made; for these I apologise, throwing myself upon the mercies of a hopefully sympathetic readership. Any additions and corrections made known to me will be most welcome and will be incorporated in any further edition that the publisher sees fit to print.

While the original intention was to list companies that built complete aircraft, lack of information about the actual products of some companies means that (particularly in the First World War), the content has certainly strayed into the component supply industry. Although this may stretch the scope of the menu beyond the taste of some, it does at least add richness to the feast.

Some firms which sound like aircraft factories may have only built parts (for example, Burton Aircraft & Manufacturing Co., and the Nottingham Aircraft Manufacturing Co.); others, which entered the industry to build parts ended up building complete machines (for example, Harris & Sheldon Ltd); finally there are those which might have done almost anything (for example, Tibbenham's Aviation Co. of Ipswich, and Warwick Aviation Co. Ltd). Once again, I must trust that any blurring of definitions as to what to include or exclude will be forgiven.

The scope of the content has also been broadened in the modern era, as I have chosen to include the contributions of a number of companies that specialise in aircraft restoration and replica construction. The scope, quality and complexity of the work undertaken by these firms exceeds, in many cases, the difficulty of the original manufacturing task. Furthermore, I wish to draw specific attention to the contribution of these organisations to the preservation of Britain's aviation heritage. Similarly, I make no apology for inclusion of a discussion of the pioneer ejection seat development work conducted by Martin-Baker Ltd at Chalgrove with its fleet of modified Meteor aircraft.

Mention must also be made of aircraft and companies that are definitely known to have existed, but for which I have been quite unable to establish a location. At the time of writing, these are:

The **Buckle** parasol monoplane. Illegally flown, unregistered, in 1929, the Buckle monoplane was constructed by Mr S.L. Buckle for the princely sum of £17. Sopwith Snipe wings, ailerons, rudder, elevator and tailplane were used. A simple rectangular section fuselage was built, and power was supplied by a 45hp six-cylinder Anzani radial. The propeller was obtained from a shed at Brooklands and cut down until the Anzani provided a satisfactory rpm. (Source: *Aeroplane Monthly*, April 1979.)

The **Newport Aircraft Co.** A question was asked in Parliament in November 1918 in relation to unpaid wages and bonuses at this company.

In addition, there are two companies whose addresses I have been unable to confirm: **Cambrian Aircraft Constructors Ltd**, and **Northwold Aircraft Co. Ltd**.

The Evolution of
the British Aircraft Industry

This section presents a summary of the overall development of the aircraft industry in Britain, highlighting specifically (in this volume) activities in Central and Eastern England. This area is notable for the extent of manufacture conducted during the First World War; the contribution of the motor industry to aircraft production in both world wars; and extensive engine flight test operations. Specific activities include:

- Sir W.G. Armstrong Whitworth Aircraft Ltd and its successors at Parkside, Whitley Abbey, Baginton and Bitteswell.
- Boulton & Paul Ltd (and Boulton Paul Aircraft Ltd) at Norwich and then at Wolverhampton.
- Britain's most successful post-war manufacturer of light aircraft, Auster Aircraft Ltd (and related companies) at Thurmaston & Rearsby.
- Shadow factories: Vickers–Armstrongs Ltd at Castle Bromwich and Rootes Securities Ltd at Blythe Bridge.
- The East Anglian contribution to the First World War, including: Boulton & Paul Ltd; Clayton & Shuttleworth Ltd; Robey & Co. Ltd; Ransomes, Sims & Jeffries Ltd; Ruston, Proctor & Co. Ltd; Savages Ltd; Mann, Egerton & Co. Ltd.
- The motor industry: Austin Motors Ltd, The Daimler Co. Ltd, Humber Motor Co. Ltd, Morris Motors Ltd, Rootes Securities Ltd, The Standard Motor Co. Ltd; Sunbeam Motor Co. Ltd; Wolseley Motors Ltd.
- Engine flight-testing by D. Napier & Son (Luton); Armstrong Siddeley Motors Ltd (Bitteswell); and Rolls-Royce Ltd (at Hucknall and Church Broughton).

The closure of airfields in this region has occurred mainly as a result of industrial relocation, reorganisation or the closure of their parent firms. This is reflected in the loss in this region of Bitteswell, Castle Bromwich, Rearsby, Seighford and Wolverhampton (Pendeford).

1
Pioneers
(1908–1914)

Flying in Europe began in France in 1906, with the flights of Santos Dumont in October and November of that year. By 1908, practical machines were being flown in France by such pioneers as Farman, Voisin and Blériot. The Wright brothers astounded their audiences with the performance and controllability of their craft when it was publicly displayed at Le Mans in the autumn of 1908. The time was now right for Britain's pioneers to take to the air.

A.V. Roe had been experimenting for some time at Brooklands, but his short flights of 8 June 1908 failed to achieve official recognition. S.F. Cody flew at Farnborough in October 1908, J.T.C. Moore-Brabazon flew at Eastchurch at the end of April 1909, and by July 1909 A.V. Roe's triplane was performing well at Lea Marshes. In February 1909, the Short brothers took a licence to manufacture Wright biplanes for the Aero Club, setting up a factory at Leysdown on the Isle of Sheppey. Britain now possessed an aircraft industry.

The pioneering period prior to the First World War was marked by adventure, experiment and innovation – the techniques of building and of flying aeroplanes were not yet understood. There was no right or wrong solution to any aspect of design, and consequently almost every possible configuration was attempted and many blind alleys were explored. Potentially good designs were let down by poor detail design, inadequate control arrangements, or heavy, inefficient and unreliable engines.

Learning often came slowly: A.V. Roe advertised throughout the First World War that he was the pioneer of the tractor biplane, although, with his initial interest in the triplane configuration, it was 1911 before his Avro D flew. F. Warren Merriam, instructor at the Bristol School, remarked on how long it took to understand that a seat belt could save lives. In a number of cases, lives were lost because pilots simply fell off their machines. Quite trivial landing accidents could also cause death and injury as a result of the pilot being thrown from an aircraft that was otherwise little damaged. It also took a considerable time before the importance of pointing into wind for take-off and landing was understood. In the technical arena, incorrect assumptions were commonplace, for example in the inadequate stressing of monoplanes against down loads. Even *Flight* is found in May 1913 expressing great surprise that the Eastbourne Aviation Co. monoplane should have adopted ailerons for lateral control when wing warping has 'become almost standard practice'.

The pioneer aircraft that have been included in this volume are, in the main, those that are known to have flown successfully. In some cases, where the fact of flight is not entirely certain, aircraft have been included which at least have the appearance that they might have flown successfully (e.g. Sanders Type 2, Beccles). Known freaks have been excluded (e.g. the Aerial Wheel Monoplane, which was built in Birmingham and entered in the 1912 Military Trials at Larkhill).

The main flying locations prior to the First World War were Brooklands, Eastchurch, Hendon and Shoreham. By comparison, pioneer activity in Central and Eastern England was rather low key.

Significant pioneer activity in this area includes:

- James Radley and W.B.R. Moorhouse at Portholme Aerodrome, Huntingdon.
- The Sanders Aeroplane Co. at Beccles.

A Humber monoplane that has come to grief at Dunstall Park, Wolverhampton. This photograph was taken on 17 June 1910. The machine was soon flying again. (Alec Brew)

- The Maxfield Monoplane flying from Castle Bromwich golf links.
- The Humber Motor Co. Ltd building their own version of the Blériot monoplane.
- The Coventry Ordnance Works Ltd, later to become part of The English Electric Co. Ltd.
- Aviation meetings at Dunstall Park racecourse, Wolverhampton, which was also used for the experimental flying of a number of machines, including the Star Engineering Monoplane.

By the outbreak of the First World War, the Short Brothers, A.V. Roe, C.R. Fairey, Frederick Handley Page, The British & Colonial Aeroplane Co. (later to become The Bristol Aeroplane Co. Ltd), Vickers Ltd, T.O.M. Sopwith, Harry Hawker and Geoffrey de Havilland were already active in the industry. Despite the diversity of the pioneering efforts, and the many bizarre and unsuccessful designs, the seeds of today's configurations, and of today's industry, were sown during this period of adventure. Great fruit was to be harvested once these seeds found the fertile ground of warfare.

2
First World War Mass Production
(1914–1918)

The First World War saw an exponential growth in aircraft production, which is a particular feature of this survey of aircraft production in Central and Eastern England. The importance of the aeroplane during the First World War, and the reasons for the rapid growth in production demand are therefore discussed in some detail below.

The Aircraft as a Machine of War

At the outbreak of the First World War, the utility of the aeroplane had only just begun to be appreciated by the Services. It was then slow, fragile and unarmed; moreover, very few were available. Thus the Royal Flying Corps (RFC) had a total of only sixty-three first line aeroplanes, with a further thirty-nine landplanes and fifty-two seaplanes available to the Royal Naval Air Service (RNAS).

The war developed into static trench warfare, with major actions or 'pushes' preceded by artillery barrages. An early use was found in reconnaissance and artillery observation, and this role became the cornerstone of military aviation. General von Below is quoted by Maurice Baring, in *Flying Corps Headquarters 1914-1918*, as stating in a memorandum: 'The main object of fighting in the air is to enable our photographic registration and photographic reconnaissance to be carried out, and at the same time to prevent that of the enemy.' The use of fighters to prevent reconnaissance operations was therefore a natural development, followed by the application of the aeroplane to bombing operations, anti-submarine patrols and operations against airships.

Changing operational roles and the rapid development of aircraft and armament meant that existing in-service types were quickly rendered obsolete. New designs were essential, and had to be rushed into large-scale production. Aircraft were flown intensively, and losses were high through both enemy action and accidents. A large-scale training activity was required to maintain a supply of pilots to the operational squadrons, giving rise to its own losses of both men and machines.

All of this required a rapid expansion of production of all types, a process hampered by the fact that many of the potential workforce were enlisting in the Services. This problem could only be solved by bringing into the production effort industrial enterprises that had no prior experience of aircraft manufacture. The furniture and motor trades were both critical in this respect, as is evident in this region. Similarly, the workforce needed to be augmented, and many women entered the production lines of the munitions factories (including the aircraft industry) for the first time.

The types that were most widely contracted out included the designs of the Royal Aircraft Factory (such as the BE2, BE12, RE8, FE2 and SE5A), training aircraft (notably the Avro 504 and DH6), Felixstowe-designed flying boats, patrol seaplanes (Short 184), and combat aircraft (Sopwith Pup, Camel, 1½ Strutter and Snipe; Bristol F.2B Fighter; AIRCO DH4, DH9, DH9A). Toward the end of the First World War significant orders were placed for the contract manufacture of long-range bomber types, such as the Handley Page O/400 and Vickers Vimy. Many of these orders were cancelled following the Armistice.

During the First World War the submarine threat resulted in the widespread use of the flying boat for anti-submarine patrol duties. These Felixstowe F.2A and F.5 are under construction by S.E. Saunders Ltd of Cowes. (Via Norman Barfield)

Manufacture of the Short 184 patrol seaplane was contracted to ten companies, of which the most important was Robey & Co. Ltd of Lincoln, where production is seen here in full swing. (Ray Hooley collection)

Loss Rates

The expansion of production during the First World War was, in truth, an enormous enterprise. Because of its significance, it is worth reflecting on some of the facts and figures associated with this accelerated production programme. As background, one needs to appreciate the intensity of air operations, and of the high rate of loss and materiel consumption involved, as indicated by the following contemporary data:

> *The average life of an aeroplane at the battlefront is not more than two months. To keep 5,000 aircraft in active commission for one year it is necessary to furnish 30,000. Each machine in the period of its activity will use at least two motors, so that 60,000 motors will be required.*
> M. Flaudin, head of the Allied Air Board
> (quoted in the American magazine *Flying*, September 1917)

These figures seem extraordinary, but closely match the levels actually achieved by the end of the conflict.

Aircraft losses in late 1918 were running at some 200 per month. In fact, aircraft destroyed by the enemy, and in training accidents, together with those that had to be scrapped as being obsolete, represented some 60 per cent of the total constructed during the war. Sadly, training exacted a heavy toll. A question in Parliament during the 1918 Air Estimates debate revealed that during 1917 more men were lost at the training schools than were lost flying on all fronts. Winston Churchill also spoke in Parliament on 4 April 1917 on the subject of the heavy losses being suffered by the RFC during training.

Data published in 1919 (in *Flight* and elsewhere) indicates that the total casualties over the whole period of the war were 6,166 killed, 7,245 wounded and 3,128 missing. A total of 330 British airmen lost their lives in April 1917, the so-called 'Bloody April'. At this time, the expected operational life of an RFC pilot was no more than seventeen and a half flying hours. Peter King in *Knights of the Air* indicates that losses in every month of 1918 were equal to the entire strength of the RFC at the start of the First World War.

The demands imposed by these short service lives and high attrition were considerable; how were the resultant production needs to be met?

Expansion of the Production Programme

Production at existing aircraft companies was rapidly expanded, and contracts were placed with established industrial concerns, particularly in the motor car and furniture trades, to boost supply. Many new companies were also founded specifically to meet this growing demand, and to provide a sub-contract infrastructure. The resultant explosion of industrial activity was truly amazing, and has been inadequately recorded.

In May 1917, less than three years after the outbreak of the First World War, the position was summarised by the 'British Comptroller of Aeronautic Supplies' in a statement to the Board of Governors of the Aero Club of America. He stated that 'there are 958 firms in England engaged on work for the British Directorate of Aeronautic Supplies, 301 of which are direct contractors and 657 are sub-contractors'. The report further states that 'the total number of hands employed by the 50 firms of most prominence is 66,700. [...] The present British budget for aeronautics in the present year totals $575,000,000' (reported in *Flying* magazine, June 1917). These are impressive figures by any standard.

The *Aviation Pocket-Book of 1919-20* listed 148 aeroplane manufacturers and many other suppliers, and commented on the adequacy of its Gazetteer thus:

> *It does not pretend to include the names of all who are accustomed to making aeroplane parts, for many firms were doing so for the period of the war only – in fact there is hardly a motor car*

or motor car accessory or wood-working firm that was not fully occupied with aviation work at the time of the Armistice. [...] Possibly, however, some names are not included that ought to be, since it is not an easy task, when compiling a directory of this nature, to ensure its being absolutely complete.

The author must echo these sentiments in respect of the present work.

Manufacture was split between aircraft manufacturers, with their own design teams, capable of producing original designs; contractors, who built established designs to order; and component suppliers. With the dispersion of production to many enterprises, it was found necessary to create a number of regional Acceptance Parks, to which contractors delivered their aircraft for inspection and acceptance. Contractors in some cases delivered wings, tail and fuselage separately by road or rail to the acceptance aerodromes, prior to assembly and flight test.

Within the area covered by this volume, the most significant aircraft manufacturing concerns (each of whom built more than 500 aircraft, with a combined total of at least 17,740 aircraft) were:

- Morgan & Co. at Leighton Buzzard.
- Hewlett & Blondeau Ltd at Leagrave.
- The Brush Electrical Engineering Co. Ltd at Loughborough.
- Clayton & Shuttleworth Ltd and Ruston, Proctor & Co. Ltd at Lincoln.
- Boulton & Paul Ltd and Mann, Egerton & Co. Ltd at Norwich.
- Ransomes, Sims & Jeffries Ltd at Ipswich.
- The Austin Motor Co. Ltd and Wolseley Motors Ltd at Birmingham.
- The Coventry-based firms: The Siddeley-Deasy Motor Car Co. Ltd; The Coventry Ordnance Works Ltd; The Daimler Co. Ltd; Humber Motor Co. Ltd; and The Standard Motor Co. Ltd.

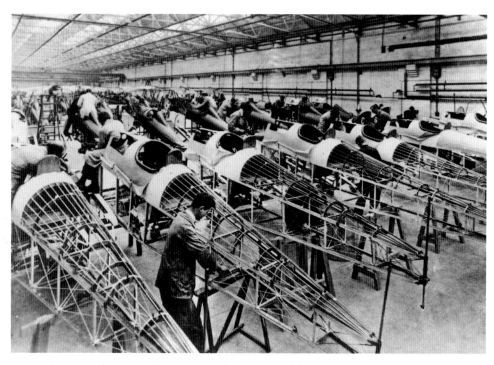

During the First World War, Wolseley Motors Ltd manufactured the BE2 and SE5A, alongside large numbers of engines and propellers. (Brooklands Museum Trust)

Production by these fifteen companies therefore represents about one third of all the aircraft built in Britain during the First World War.

Smaller concerns included: Frederick Sage & Co. Ltd at Peterborough; Portholme Aerodrome Co. at Huntingdon; Robey & Co. Ltd at Lincoln; Richard Garrett & Sons at Ipswich; and the three Birmingham-based companies of The Birmingham & Midland Carriage Co., The Metropolitan Carriage, Wagon & Finance Co., and Harris & Sheldon Ltd.

Production Quantities

The achievements of the rapidly expanding industry were remarkable. This is illustrated rather graphically by the following statement made by Winston Churchill, Minister of Munitions, speaking in Parliament on 25 April 1918, when presenting the Estimates of the Ministry of Munitions:

> We are now making in a single week more aeroplanes than were made in the whole of 1914, in a single month more than were made in the whole of 1915, and in a single quarter more than were made in the whole of 1916.

The total British production during the First World War is widely reported as 55,093 airframes (other figures are also quoted, see below), with an additional 3,051 purchased abroad. Very significant production was also undertaken in France and the USA, with American production running at around 12,000 aircraft per year by the end of the war. Data published after the First World War (as a Parliamentary Paper on 24 April 1919) gave the following figures for British production.

First World War Aircraft Production

Period	Duration (months)	Aircraft built	Aircraft per month
August 1914 to May 1915	10	530	53
June 1915 to February 1917	21	7,137	340
March 1917 to December 1917	10	13,521	1,352
January 1918 to October 1918	10	26,685	2,669

(Note: This gives a total of 47,873, some 7,200 less than is given by more recent sources.)

The expansion in production is also reflected in the numbers of aircraft on charge with the RFC and RNAS: August 1914, 272; January 1917, 5,496; January 1918, 11,091; October 1918 (RAF), 22,171. These figures, from the same source as the production numbers, show that in four years the aircraft establishment of the flying services had been increased more than eighty-fold, with the production rate increasing more than fifty-fold. To provide a comparison with United Kingdom production, one should acknowledge that this enormous acceleration in the field of aviation was evident among all combatants.

Production Difficulties

Significant production difficulties were encountered (and re-encountered in the Second World War) due to the difficulty of building up production among a large number of dispersed and sometimes inexperienced contractors and sub-contractors. The requirement to accelerate production was hampered by the steady depletion of the workforce as more and more were called up for service in France. Near-continuous industrial unrest resulted due to the heavy demands on the individual, and the Defence of the Realm Act was much used to maintain stability in the munitions industries.

Engine suppliers had great difficulty maintaining pace with airframe manufacture. Early in 1915 a serious shortage of 90hp RAF engines occurred leaving Armstrong Whitworth with no less than 100 engineless BE2 machines hanging three or four deep from the ceiling. Similarly, in January 1918, no less than 400 SE5A were waiting for engines. The lower-than-expected performance of the Siddeley Puma proved to be a problem for the DH4. Martinsyde F.3 production was reduced because of the need for Rolls-Royce Falcon engines to power the Bristol Fighter. The lack of availability of Falcon engines resulted in the Bristol Fighter being flown (with variable success) with 300hp Hispano Suiza, Siddeley Puma and Sunbeam Arab engines. Production of the FE2D was also constrained by the shortage of supply of its Rolls-Royce Eagle engine. The 200hp Hispano Suiza engine fitted to the Sopwith Dolphin suffered from frequent connecting-rod failures. The supply of engines was further hampered by the need to create a new industry to supply magnetos, the manufacture of which, until the outbreak of the First World War, had been the almost exclusive province of German industry.

At the end of the First World War, engine orders were running at around 65,000 per year, more than 8,500 of these orders being for the disastrous ABC Dragonfly. F. Warren Merriam commented, 'There is no doubt that at this late stage in the war, our aero engines were becoming less and less reliable.' Shortages affected nearly every type. Standardisation was absent; in early 1918, Mr Pemberton Billing pointed out that forty-four different types of engine were in use. Ironically, the attempt to standardise on the Dragonfly was an ignominious failure. In 1918, with vast numbers of engines on order from thirteen contractors, the Dragonfly was achieving a typical engine life of only two and a half hours before failure.

Scarcity of Resources

The needs of aircraft production resulted in a tremendous drain on resources, and even had an impact on the agricultural landscape, through the demand for flax to supply the need for aircraft linen. In July 1917, Dr Addison, Minister of Munitions, gave a specific indication of the strategic requirements of the aircraft industry:

> The fact that no fewer than 1,000 factories are engaged on some process or other connected with the construction and equipment of the flying machine proves the magnitude of the work we have in hand. The needs of the aeroplane programme are enormous, almost passing belief. For our present programme of construction, more spruce is required than the present annual output of the United States, more mahogany than Honduras can supply – and Honduras is accustomed to supply the requirements of the World. Besides this, all the linen of the type required made in Ireland, the home of the linen industry, and the whole of the alloyed steel that England can produce can be used. As for flax, the Government has actually to provide the seed from which to grow the plant essential for its purposes.

Flax seed was supplied free to growers, who were further encouraged with significant subsidies, and guaranteed prices. The scheme was administered by the Flax Production Branch of the Board of Agriculture. Further financial assistance to growers was offered in July 1918 as a result of the Flax Companies (Financial Assistance) Bill. So successful were these measures that by the time of the Armistice, production of aircraft fabric was running at 7 million yards (nearly 4,000 miles) per month. By April 1919, the Ministry of Munitions had in stock and available for disposal no less than 31,970,725 yards of linen. In mid-1919, the total surplus (by now 40,000,000 yards, or nearly 23,000 miles of fabric, in sixteen varieties and widths of between 25 to 72 inches) was sold to one individual, Mr J.L. Martin, for about £4,000,000.

The Government requested in late 1917 that farmers carry out a census of ash trees, where potential supply problems were causing some concern. In supporting this request it was stated that 'The Government requirements for the next 12 months [i.e. 1918] are expected to exceed 200,000 trees'. In all, about one third of the volume of timber standing at the outbreak of war was felled, much being used in aircraft manufacture.

Overall, perhaps the most striking feature of the First World War mass production effort was that the entire enterprise, involving more than a thousand companies, was created within ten years of the construction of Britain's first aeroplane.

Foundation of the SBAC

On 23 March 1916, the main constructing firms came together to form an interest group through which to voice their common concerns. This was the Society of British Aircraft Constructors (SBAC), an organisation that continues to be a spokesman for the industry today. The founder members include a significant number of firms that are less than familiar today. The initial list of forty founder members, as published in April 1916, was:

Aircraft Manufacturing Co. Ltd
Airships Ltd
The Austin Motor Co. (1914) Ltd
Wm Beardmore & Co. Ltd
The Blackburn Aeroplane & Motor Co. Ltd
Boulton & Paul Ltd
The Brush Electrical Engineering Co. Ltd
The Coventry Ordnance Works Ltd
The Daimler Co. Ltd
Darracq Motor Engineering Co. Ltd
Wm. Denny & Brothers
The Dudbridge Iron Works Ltd
The Grahame-White Aviation Co. Ltd
Handley Page Ltd
Hewlett & Blondeau Ltd
Jouques Aviation Works
Mann & Grimmer
Mann, Egerton & Co. Ltd
Martinsyde Ltd
D. Napier & Son, Ltd

Parnall & Sons
Phoenix Dynamo Manufacturing Co. Ltd
A.V. Roe & Co. Ltd
Robey & Co. Ltd
Ruston, Proctor & Co. Ltd
Frederick Sage & Co. Ltd
S.E. Saunders Ltd
Short Bros
The Siddeley-Deasy Motor Car Co. Ltd
The Sopwith Aviation Co. Ltd
The Standard Motor Co. Ltd
The Sunbeam Motor Car Co. Ltd
The Norman Thompson Flight Co. Ltd
Vickers Ltd
G. & J. Weir Ltd
Wells Aviation Co. Ltd
Westland Aircraft Works
J. Samuel White & Co. Ltd
Whitehead Aircraft Co. Ltd
Wolseley Motors Ltd.

This group of companies, plus a few others which joined the SBAC shortly thereafter (such as Sir W.G. Armstrong, Whitworth & Co. Ltd) made up the aircraft industry at the end of the First World War. Fourteen of the founder members of the SBAC are to be found in the area covered by this volume. Not a single company in the above list survives today, as a wholly British aircraft manufacturer, although Shorts (as a subsidiary of Bombardier) and AgustaWestland (shortly to be wholly owned by the Italian firm Finmeccanica) are honourable near-survivors.

3
Collapse and Re-birth
Between the Wars
(1919–1939)

The inter-war period was marked by the near-complete collapse of the military aircraft market, and the return of the majority of contractors to their original products and markets. The larger companies were restructured to avoid Excess Profit Duty, and they all faced competition from their own products, now being marketed by The Aircraft Disposal Co. Military sales were very limited in number.

In the 1930s, the light aircraft movement resulted in expansion of civil production, and many new concerns were established, only to be cut off at the start of the Second World War. The de Havilland Aircraft Co. Ltd found a sustained civil market with a succession of designs following on from the ground-breaking DH60 Moth. Taylorcraft Aeroplanes (England) Ltd and Percival Aircraft Ltd both succeeded and were able to make a valuable contribution to Britain's efforts during the Second World War. Military re-armament began in 1935, and provided a lifeline for the main manufacturers.

Post-war Collapse

What brought about the collapse? Quite simply, the need for aircraft evaporated virtually overnight. Once the war stopped, the country had neither the resources, nor the need, to sustain the aircraft production juggernaut. Many orders were cancelled, and the enormous stock of war surplus aircraft was sold on favourable terms to The Aircraft Disposal Co. at Croydon. In consequence, any firm attempting a new aircraft venture during the immediate post-war period inevitably found itself competing with its own, or its competitors', second-hand products.

When this difficulty was combined with the effects of Excess Profits Duty, it is not surprising that wholesale reorganisation took place. Most of the sub-contractors either went into liquidation or returned to their former trades. In this region, the East Anglian contractors, with the exception of Boulton & Paul Ltd, ceased aircraft manufacture, whilst the automotive industy in Birmingham and Coventry returned to its accustomed trade. The prime contractors also reorganised, slimmed down, or went into liquidation; many flirted with the motor trade and other forms of diversification. A number of those that entered voluntary liquidation emerged in new, fitter, guises to carry on in the aircraft business. The survivors drew the protective cloak of the SBAC tightly around themselves.

The scale of the contraction after the Armistice was incredible. On 11 November 1918, 25,000 aircraft were on order. The Air Ministry sought to shut down production of all obsolete types immediately, and only accept delivery of those contracts from which they positively could not extricate themselves. Those obsolete types that could not be cancelled would be sent directly to store. By cancellation of these orders, the number of aircraft that the Ministry was obliged to accept was reduced to 13,432. Scrapping for the recovery of useful parts proved not to be very economic, and it was recommended that greater savings would be made if the engine were to be removed, and the rest of the machine burned.

By the end of 1920, the Aircraft Manufacturing Co. Ltd (AIRCO), The British & Colonial Aeroplane Co. Ltd, Nieuport & General Aircraft Co. Ltd, Martinsyde Ltd, The Central

Aircraft Co., The Grahame-White Aviation Co. Ltd and Sopwith Aviation & Engineering Co. Ltd had variously closed, entered receivership, or reorganised. By June 1922 only ninety-seven British civil aircraft had Certificates of Airworthiness, down from 240 in 1920. By the mid-1920s, the industry had reduced to sixteen major manufacturers: Sir W.G. Armstrong Whitworth Aircraft Ltd; A.V. Roe & Co. Ltd; The Blackburn Aeroplane & Motor Co. Ltd; Boulton & Paul Ltd; The Bristol Aeroplane Co. Ltd; The de Havilland Aircraft Co. Ltd; Fairey Aviation Ltd; The Gloucestershire Aircraft Co. Ltd; Handley Page Ltd; H.G. Hawker Enginering Co. Ltd; George Parnall & Co. Ltd; S.E. Saunders Ltd; Short Brothers (Rochester & Bedford) Ltd; The Supermarine Aviation Works Ltd; Vickers Ltd; Westland Aircraft Works (Branch of Petters Ltd).

Military Production in the 1920s and 1930s

From this point onwards, military aircraft manufacture was virtually reduced to the modification and development of the existing in-service types, and the development of a smattering of prototypes. The prototype activity was spread across the industry and just about sustained the industrial base. The lack of active operations meant that only small production volumes of largely obsolescent aircraft were required to fulfil the needs of the RAF. Shorts, for example, built less than forty aircraft during the whole of the 1920s.

Within this region Boulton & Paul Ltd (latterly Boulton Paul Aircraft Ltd) built its own designs in small numbers and also supplied the RAF with a modest quantity of Sidestrand and Overstrand bombers. This company was, however, not wholly dependent upon aircraft production. Contract production of 106 Hawker Demon aircraft supplemented production of Boulton Paul's own designs until the late 1930s saw the transition to production of the Defiant and contract production of the Blackburn Roc. The other major manufacturer in this region was Sir W.G. Armstrong Whitworth Aircraft Ltd. This company was able to sustain higher production levels, with its own Siskin and Atlas, and contract production of the Hawker Hart/Hart Trainer. Expansion of the RAF then resulted in large-scale production of the Whitley bomber from 1936 onward.

One measure of the desperation of the industry was that key military requirements, likely to lead to significant production contracts, would lead to a rash of official and private venture prototypes being produced. An example is provided by the influential requirement F.7/30 for a new fighter aircraft, issued in 1931. The aircraft that competed for a contract against this requirement were as follows:

- Blackburn F.7/30 (K2892)
- Bristol Type 123 biplane (private venture, unmarked)
- Bristol Type 133 monoplane (private venture, R-10)
- Gloster SS.37 (private venture, G.37) – eventually ordered into production as the Gladiator
- Hawker (private venture, I-PV3)
- Supermarine F.7/30 (K2890)
- Westland F.7/30 (K2891)

Four of the seven types flown were constructed on a private venture basis, and none of the three officially funded designs was selected.

Specification F.7/30, in addition to producing the RAF's last biplane fighter, was also instrumental in the genesis of the Supermarine Spitfire. R.J. Mitchell's proposal for an improved solution to this requirement led to funding for the development of a new design (the Type 300) against a modified specification (F.37/34). This specification was superseded by F.10/35, which the Type 300 was modified to meet (although the aircraft was still referred to by the firm as the F.37/34). F.10/35 sought a fighter aircraft with eight guns and a speed

The Boulton Paul Overstrand was the first RAF type to be fitted with a gun turret and was a development of the company's earlier Sidestrand design. (Ken Ellis collection)

Seven types were built for competition against Specification F.7/30 and, although none entered production, this requirement was to prove influential in the genesis of the Supermarine Spitfire. This is the Westland design K2891 photographed prior to its first flight. (Westland)

advantage over 'the contemporary bomber' of at least 40mph at 15,000ft. A speed of 310mph was required at the same altitude, with an enclosed cockpit providing a good pilot field of view, particularly in the upper hemisphere. Thus was the Spitfire, as the Air Ministry subsequently named the type, born.

The military market remained stagnant until, during the late 1930s, tension rose within Europe leading to progressive re-armament from 1935. From this point onward, the military manufacturers saw increasing orders and the start of sub-contract/dispersed production to increase capacity.

Civil Production and the Light Aeroplane Movement

Immediately after the First World War, there were limited attempts to generate an air transport market, with A.V. Roe & Co. Ltd (Avro Transport Service), Blackburn (North Sea Aerial Navigation Co. Ltd), Handley Page (Handley Page Transport Ltd) and AIRCO (Aircraft Transport & Travel Ltd) all starting airline services, mainly using converted military aircraft. These efforts were unsuccessful and, although small numbers of commercial aircraft were sold to independent airlines, there was no real demand for air travel. Even after the formation of Imperial Airways, airliner production in Britain was restricted to modest production runs from Armstrong Whitworth, de Havilland, Handley Page, and Shorts. Armstrong Whitworth produced the Argosy (1926, seven built); Atalanta (1932, eight built); and Ensign (1938, fourteen built).

The appearance of the de Havilland Dragon (1932) and Dragon Rapide (1934) saw production quantities increase. It is fair to say, however, that, with the exception of de Havilland, and Empire flying boat production at Shorts, military aircraft production dominated the affairs of most of the larger companies.

Airliner production between the wars was limited to that required to meet the needs of Imperial Airways. Only eight examples were built of the relatively clean Atalanta of 1932. (BAE SYSTEMS plc via Ray Williams)

The Auster I was produced by Taylorcraft Aeroplanes (England) Ltd, which evolved into Auster Aircraft Ltd, Britain's most successful post-war manufacturer of light aircraft. (Author)

The Luton Minor is a notable pre-war design that, like the Currie Wot, has been taken up by the home-built aircraft movement under the administration of the Popular Flying Association. (Author)

While the Lympne Light Aeroplane Trials of 1924 and 1926 generated much publicity for the potential of privately owned aircraft, the competing aircraft themselves were not a great success. The appearance of the de Havilland Moth, and the availability of subsidies for flying schools, radically changed this picture. New companies emerged and prospered, including the famous names of Airspeed (at York and then Portsmouth), de Havilland (initially at Stag Lane, and then Hatfield), General Aircraft (Croydon and then Hanworth), Percival Aircraft (Gravesend and then Luton), and Miles (then as Phillips & Powis (Aircraft) Ltd, at Woodley). Much of this activity was concentrated in, and near, London, as flying gathered popularity as a fashionable activity.

One notable firm in this region was Taylorcraft Aeroplanes (England) Ltd at Thurmaston. This company was founded in 1938, with the result that only limited sales were achieved before the outbreak of the Second World War. Selected for Army Air Observation Post duties, the Taylorcraft Plus D (or Auster I) provided a springboard for the later success of Auster Aircraft Ltd, Britain's most successful post-war aircraft manufacturer.

A new phenomenon also arose in the form of the craze for the Flying Flea sparked by the design of the tandem wing *Pou de Ciel* by Henri Mignet. Although ultimately (and in some cases tragically) unsuccessful, the Flea served to legitimise the eccentric British habit of constructing home-built aircraft. This had originated in the pioneering period by the enthusiasm of the likes of Mr Jezzi at Eastchurch, being continued after the First World War by such characters as F.H. Lowe at Heaton, and the Blake brothers at Winchester. This tradition has been carried on to this day in Britain by individuals such as John Isaacs, John Taylor, Ivan Shaw and many others, now under the very professional administration of the Popular Flying Association.

4
Second World War Mass Production (1939–1945)

Rearmament and the Shadow Factory Scheme

The expansion of the aircraft production programme against the threat of war built up gradually from 1935 and is inseparably linked to the Second World War aircraft production effort. While, to many eyes, the move to re-arm Britain's forces came perilously late, moves began some five years before the Second World War broke out. The first step was the adoption of an expansion plan in July 1934, known as Scheme A, to increase the size of the Royal Air Force. Under this scheme the Metropolitan Air Force was intended to grow to 1,252 operational aircraft by the spring of 1939.

Hitler had become Chancellor in January 1933, but his repudiation of the Treaty of Versailles, reoccupation of the Rhineland, the Austrian Anschluss, the annexation of Czechoslovakia and the Nazi-Soviet Pact were still years ahead. It is clear, therefore, that some early positive decisions were made and as a result the armaments industry began to grow. The real difficulty lay in the lack of investment in modern designs and technology, combined with the drastic reduction in production capacity caused by the lean years of the 1920s and early 1930s.

The pace of re-armament in the aircraft industry quickened with Scheme C, which was instituted in May 1935 and which brought about further significant increases in both the size of the RAF, and the production of new aircraft types. From October 1936 the need for increased production led to the formation of the 'shadow factory' scheme. New factories were constructed using public funds, owned by the Government, but run by private industry to boost the production of (initially) aero engine components, where the shortfall in production capacity was even more marked than in the airframe industry. The contractual complexities of the shadow factory scheme introduce uncertainty in some instances over the precise responsibility for site management and aircraft production/assembly at particular sites. This is an area that would benefit from further research.

In addition to Bristol (whose engines were to be produced), the five companies initially involved in the shadow factory scheme were Austin Motor Co. Ltd, The Daimler Co. Ltd, Rootes Securities Ltd (Humber), The Rover Company Ltd and the Standard Motor Co. Ltd. In February 1937 the scheme was extended to allow Austin and Rootes to construct airframes as well as engines. Despite this early recognition that engine availability was critical to the acceleration of airframe production, there were periods, as in the First World War, when engineless airframes were in plentiful supply.

The early expansion schemes favoured light day bombers such as the Fairey Battle and Vickers Wellesley. Unfortunately, the concept of the light day bomber proved to be a blind alley, with the Battle, in particular, suffering from high operational losses whilst trying to stem the Blitzkrieg across the Low Countries during 1940. (Fairey Battle losses between 10 and 14 May 1940 were sixty aircraft, out of the 108 deployed operationally, during attacks against troop concentrations and the Albert Canal bridges.) Other types that entered production in this period included the Hampden, Whitley and Blenheim. These types were to make an important contribution in the early years of the Second World War, but lacked the performance and payload to remain in front-line service throughout the coming conflict. From

The Armstrong Whitworth Whitley was brought into service as a result of the pre-war expansion of the RAF. Production Whitley V N1352 displays the characteristic nose down attitude of the type in flight. (Ray Williams archive)

Spitfire F.22 fuselage assembly at Castle Bromwich. This enormous factory produced more Spitfires than all the other factories producing the type put together. (Richard R. Leader via Geoff Negus)

Something of the scale of the wartime production effort can be inferred from this picture of Austin-built Lancaster noses awaiting final assembly. (via Geoff Negus)

1936 onward, types such as the Wellington, Hurricane and Spitfire began to be ordered in quantity through parent and shadow factories. Later on, the focus switched to heavy bomber production (particularly the Halifax and Lancaster), anticipating the need for a bomber offensive against Germany.

Wartime saw an increase in activity in Central and Eastern England, due in part to the establishment of additional production capacity to supplement that of the major aircraft firms. Examples include:

- Vickers-Armstrongs Ltd (Supermarine) with a large shadow factory at Castle Bromwich (supported by a number of local outstations). (This factory was initially created under the supervision of the Nuffield Organisation, at which time its management was provided by staff from Morris Motors Ltd.) Generally known as CBAF, this factory was officially Vickers-Armstrongs Ltd Castle Bromwich Works.
- Tiger Moth production was transferred to Morris Motors at Cowley to allow The de Havilland Aircraft Co. Ltd to concentrate its resources on the Mosquito. DH89 Dominie production was undertaken by Brush Coachworks at Loughborough, and Mosquito production by Standard Motors at Coventry/Ansty.
- Austin Motors Ltd of Birmingham built the Fairey Battle day bomber. This company went on to build the Hawker Hurricane fighter and the Short Stirling and Avro Lancaster heavy bombers.
- Rootes Securities Ltd at Blythe Bridge provided additional capacity for the production of the Bristol Blenheim and Beaufighter.

Elsewhere, Sir W.G. Armstrong Whitworth Aircraft Ltd created additional production capacity at Baginton and Bitteswell. Hawker capacity was increased with operations at Langley supplementing those at Kingston and Brooklands. Gloster Aircraft Co. Ltd was used to provide additional Hurricane production capacity and to take responsibility for the Henley and Typhoon. Vickers Wellington production at Brooklands/Weybridge was supplemented by factories at Broughton (Chester) and Blackpool. A.V. Roe & Co. Ltd began operations at Yeadon; Blackburn Aircraft Ltd reinstated production at Sherburn-in-Elmet and Dumbarton; and Fairey Aviation added production capacity at Heaton Chapel and Errwood Park. The London Aircraft Production Group (at Aldenham and Leavesden) and The English Electric Co. Ltd (at Preston/Samlesbury) added to the output of Halifax bombers produced by Handley Page Ltd at Radlett. The heavy bomb damage sustained at Rochester resulted in production of the Short Stirling at Swindon and South Marston and the setting up of a production line at Short & Harland Ltd in Belfast.

Production Difficulties

Large-scale orders and expanded capacity were one thing: production proved to be quite another problem. Production difficulties were encountered with the accelerating demands placed on both airframe and engine manufacturers, particularly as the British industry was only just accommodating retractable undercarriages, variable pitch propellers, and all-metal stressed skin monoplanes. In contemporary reports one finds reference to:

- Poorly organised initial production of the Spitfire by Supermarine at Woolston, with mismatched wing and fuselage production rates.
- Similar problems at Filton with the Blenheim, with thirty-two fuselages produced before any wings appeared.
- The initial inability of the Morris-run Castle Bromwich shadow factory to get the Spitfire into production.
- Miles Master development and production dictated by availability of particular engine types.
- Master, Oxford and Tiger Moth airframes dispersed into storage to await their engines.
- Fairey's problems of excessive dispersal of its factories, including delays to the Albacore due to problems with its Taurus engine. The delays to Albacore production led to a further delay of about a year in establishing Firefly production. A delay of two years to the Barracuda was attributed to priority being given to other types in production by Fairey at Heaton Chapel and Errwood Park. Sir Stafford Cripps intervened to introduce new personnel and reorganise project management at Fairey Aviation.
- Bristol's engineless Beaufighters towed by road from the factory at Filton to Whitchurch to await completion.
- Production levels in 1937/38 running at around one third of those planned for the Battle and Blenheim, and virtually zero for the Spitfire.
- Dozens of Typhoons at Brockworth without engines being ferried to maintenance units using 'slave' engines. The engines were then removed, sent back to the Gloster factory, and refitted to the next aircraft for its delivery.

The setting up of the shadow factory scheme was, itself, a drain on the resources of the parent firms, due to their need to produce additional drawings and tooling, and to provide oversight of the expansion factories. One should not, however, forget the scale of the task, and the depleted production resource initially available for the effort.

Production Quantities and Standardisation

Despite all these difficulties, expansion in the immediate pre-war period was more successful than has been widely acknowledged. 1n 1935, 893 military aircraft were produced. This figure was more than doubled in 1936, and by 1939 reached 7,940, a nearly nine-fold increase in only five years. In 1941, the figure was more than 20,000, and by 1944 it exceeded 26,000.

The main production effort during the Second World War was split between the following organisations:

- The main design firms of A.V. Roe & Co. Ltd, Sir W.G. Armstrong Whitworth Aircraft Ltd, Blackburn Aircraft Ltd, Bristol Aeroplane Co. Ltd, The de Havilland Aircraft Co. Ltd, The Fairey Aviation Co. Ltd, Gloster Aircraft Co. Ltd, Handley Page Ltd, Hawker Aircraft Ltd, Short Brothers (Rochester & Bedford) Ltd, Vickers-Armstrongs Ltd, and Westland Aircraft Ltd.
- Shadow and dispersed factories controlled either by aircraft industry parent firms, or by the motor industry (Rootes Securities Ltd, The Austin Motor Co. Ltd, Morris Motors Ltd, Standard Motor Co. Ltd, etc), mainly in the Midlands and the north west of England. This activity includes contract production by The English Electric Co. Ltd at Preston and Samlesbury (Hampden, Halifax and Vampire), London Aircraft Production Group at Leavesden (Halifax) and Short & Harland Ltd in Belfast (Bombay, Hereford, Sunderland and Stirling).
- Smaller companies such as Airspeed (1934) Ltd, Cunliffe-Owen Aircraft Ltd, Folland Aircraft Ltd, Heston Aircraft Ltd, Phillips & Powis (Aircraft) Ltd/Miles Aircraft Ltd, Percival Aircraft Ltd, and Taylorcraft Aeroplanes (England) Ltd.
- Firms within the Civilian Repair Organisation such as Marshall of Cambridge, Morrisons, Brooklands Aviation Ltd, and many others; manufacturers' Repair Organisations such as SEBRO at Cambridge; and RAF Maintenance Units such as Henlow and Kemble. Many aircraft that were nominally repaired and returned to service were substantially new airframes by the time that 'repair' had been completed.

The risk of bomb damage to main factory sites led every firm to set up dispersed operations. As in the First World War, large numbers of firms were involved, and as early as mid-1939, some 1,200 companies were involved in sub-contract aircraft production. Peak production in the Second World War reached 2,715 aircraft per month (March 1944), with, in addition, more than 500 aircraft per month returned to service after repair.

Unlike the First World War, there was a general policy of limiting the number of types in production. The increased efficiency and production volume that resulted offset the loss of some potentially outstanding designs (such as the Martin-Baker MB5, the production of which was blocked). As production gathered momentum, a number of companies were diverted from building their own types in favour of the standardised designs. Examples in this area include production of the Avro Lancaster and Avro Lincoln by Sir W.G. Armstrong Whitworth Aircraft Ltd, and production of the Fairey Barracuda by Boulton Paul Aircraft Ltd.

The main Second World War production types are summarised in the following table:

Main Second World War Production Types

Fighter	Bomber	Trainer/Liaison	Other
Defiant	Hampden	Tiger Moth	Swordfish
Hurricane	Battle	Oxford	Sunderland
Spitfire	Blenheim	Master	Firefly
Typhoon	Wellington	Magister	Seafire

Standardisation on a limited number of types resulted in large production runs for the Spitfire and Lancaster (here at Castle Bromwich in spring 1944), together with the Hurricane, Wellington, Mosquito and Halifax. (Richard R. Leader via Geoff Negus)

Fighter	Bomber	Trainer/Liaison	Other
Tempest	Stirling	Anson	Walrus
Beaufighter	Halifax	Auster	Lysander
	Lancaster	Proctor	Beaufort
	Mosquito	Dominie	Barracuda

By about 1941, most of the production capacity for front-line machines had been grouped on the Stirling, Halifax and Lancaster bombers, the Beaufighter, the Mosquito, the Spitfire, and the Barracuda. The reduced number of types produced reflects the technical maturity of the industry; it was no longer possible for the enemy to produce a new design that would completely change the balance of air power overnight. The Messerschmitt Me262 might have had such an effect had it been available earlier and in larger numbers, but in general it was found that progressive improvement of existing designs could keep pace with new enemy designs. Thus, the Spitfire was able to maintain its operational utility, through progressive engine, carburation and airframe developments, in the face of the Focke Wulf Fw190 and its developments.

Figures released at the end of the war by the Ministry of Aircraft Production stated that wartime production totalled some 125,000 complete aircraft, largest numbers being (in sequence) Spitfire, Hurricane, Wellington, Anson, Lancaster, Mosquito, Halifax, Beaufighter, Blenheim and Oxford (all 5,000 aircraft or more). (Note that the total figure is undoubtedly

The DH82A Tiger Moth was key to the provision of pilots from the EFTS programme. This example was built at Cowley by Morris Motors Ltd. (Author)

larger than is given above, as the published list does not include non–operational types such as the Tiger Moth, more than 8,800 of which were built.)

It is also worth noting, in the light of the post–war domination of the industry by the USA, that although starting later, the US industrial machine outstripped UK production by a comfortable margin. The US built some 360,000 aircraft in the Second World War, nearly 96,000 of them in 1944 alone.

5
Post-war
(1945–1960)

When peace came, the various Government-owned shadow factories were no longer required for aircraft production, and were closed, or converted for car and engine manufacture. The aircraft industry set about meeting the challenges that it faced. These were the relatively unfamiliar demands of the commercial market, and the race to exploit the new technologies of war as tensions mounted between the West and the Soviet Bloc. The industry's efforts were made more difficult by the weakness of Britain's war-shattered economy. Although the conditions facing the industry were not as drastic as those after the First World War, some companies still found themselves diversifying into new products. In this region, as with the period immediately after the First World War, many of the contract manufacturers, particularly in the motor industry, simply returned to their original trade.

Commercial Aircraft Developments

A key decision, which has shaped the post-war commercial aircraft industry, was that wartime transport aircraft production was allocated to the USA. As a result, the excellent C-47 Dakota or DC-3 was immediately available for opening up the post-war air routes, with longer range services provided by the DC-4 (C-54 Skymaster), the later DC-6 and the Lockheed Constellation. Not only were these excellent aircraft in their own right, but they also proved capable of development into a line of successful derivative aircraft.

What then of Britain? New aircraft types were needed – Britain's pre-war airliners had, after all, not exactly led the world in their performance or technology. Despite the strain on the economy, an attempt was made, through the Brabazon Committee, to identify and develop a fleet of new aircraft covering a wide range of commercial applications. Unfortunately, these designs could not be created overnight, and, in the short-term, stop-gap designs and converted bombers were all that was available to compete for airline markets. Worse was to follow, as when the new types appeared, they were (with a couple of notable exceptions) not well suited to the prevailing market conditions. One common fault seems to have been the specification of too few passenger seats. Perhaps this reflected the view that few people could afford to fly, and those that could, would expect a suitably civilised environment!

To modern eyes, and admittedly with the benefit of hindsight, the first post-war commercial offerings from British industry seem brave but, in many cases, doomed from the outset. Among these were:

- The hurriedly converted bombers – the Lancastrian, Halton, and Stirling V.
- Britain's only true transport of the war, the Avro York – itself a development of the Lancaster bomber.
- The Sunderland flying boat conversions and developments – the Hythe, Sandringham and Solent.
- Non-starters – Armstrong Whitworth Apollo, Bristol Brabazon, Cunliffe-Owen Concordia, Portsmouth Aerocar, Percival Merganser, and Saunders-Roe Princess.
- The honourable exceptions – the new designs that reached production. These were

Only two examples of the Mamba-powered Armstrong Whitworth Apollo were completed. (Ray Williams)

The British Britannia was an efficient and popular tansport, but suffered from protracted development and the early appearance of jet competition. (Author)

Production of the Prince, Sea Prince, Pembroke and President totalled nearly 200 aircraft. This Prince 6 was photographed at Baginton in less-than-pristine condition. (Author)

the Airspeed Ambassador, Avro Tudor, Bristol Freighter, Bristol Britannia,
de Havilland Comet, de Havilland Dove, Handley Page Hermes, Handley Page
(Reading) Marathon, Percival Prince, Vickers Viking and Vickers Viscount.

Sadly, the vast majority could not compete with the operational economics of the American designs, nor the economies of scale afforded by the US industrial machine. Of British commercial aircraft in the immediate post-war period, only the de Havilland Dove and the Vickers Viscount were unqualified successes. It is indeed tragic that the Comet, which could have achieved a generation of British leadership in the skies, proved to be unexpectedly flawed. Although redesign of the Comet eventually produced a robust and successful aircraft, the moment had been lost as far as British domination of the commercial air transport market was concerned.

Military Aircraft Programmes

On the military side, the defeat of Germany and Japan brought peace, but no reduction in tension because of the development of the 'Cold War' with the Soviet Union. The end of the war had seen the development of long-range surface-to-surface rockets, jet and rocket-propelled aircraft, and the atomic bomb. German technical progress with the development of the thin swept wing had also opened the door to much higher speeds, and the prospect of supersonic flight. Britain, and indeed the whole developed world, therefore plunged into a race to develop and exploit these technologies in the military field.

Britain's brilliant lead in jet engine technology saw operational fruit with the Meteor and Vampire, but was rapidly surpassed by the pace of development in both the USA and the USSR. In these nations, the significance of German swept-wing developments was better understood and acted upon, resulting in the superlative Sabre and Mikoyan & Guryevich MiG 15/17. Despite 'super-priority' programmes, Britain was unable to bring its own Swift or the Hunter quickly into service, and had to suffer the indignity of the interim operation of the F-86 Sabre in order to preserve a credible operational capability. Naval aviation relied upon the propeller-driven Sea Hornet, Sea Fury and Wyvern with jets being introduced in the form of the Attacker, Sea Venom, Sea Hawk and DH110 Sea Vixen. As the 1950s came to an end, Britain began the development of V/STOL combat aircraft with initial trials of the P.1127, which was to lead, via the Kestrel, to the production of the Harrier close support aircraft.

In the field of bombers, the superb Canberra was flown in 1949 and continues in RAF service in 2004, more than fifty years later. The Canberra was followed by the challenging V-Bomber programme, which demonstrated that Britain could indeed produce world-class designs. How extraordinary, however, that after all its deprivations in the Second World War, the country could actually afford to carry all three V-Bombers – the Valiant, Victor and Vulcan – into production in the face of the Cold War threat. Central and Eastern England soon reverberated to the sound of the V-force – the first Valiant base was Gaydon in Warwickshire, and several other RAF stations in this area were to receive these impressive types into service.

Transport and training aircraft programmes also delivered some long serving types including the Vickers Valetta and Varsity, Handley Page Hastings, Blackburn Beverley, de Havilland Devon and Chipmunk, and the Percival/Hunting Percival Prentice, Pembroke and Provost.

Westland transitioned to the manufacture of helicopters based upon the licence-built construction of Sikorsky designs, initially in the form of the WS-51 Dragonfly, and the WS-55 Whirlwind. A wider rotorcraft industry developed with a range of home-grown designs from Bristol (Sycamore and Belvedere), Fairey (Ultra-Light, Gyrodyne and Rotodyne) and Saunders-Roe (Skeeter and P.531).

In the general aviation field, Auster Aircraft Ltd (previously Taylorcraft Aeroplanes (England) Ltd) achieved rare success with an extensive range of types developed progressively from its wartime AOP machines. Numerous ex-military aircraft (particularly the AOP. Mk V) were converted to civil use. Production followed of more than 400 Auster Autocrat; more than 200 Aiglet and Aiglet Trainer; and more than 200 of the Autocar series, all predominantly for civil use. Military production included more than 400 Auster AOP. Mk 6 and T. Mk 7, and 167 Auster AOP. Mk 9.

It now seems incredible that Britain should simultaneously produce three completely different types of strategic bomber – the V-bomber force. Vulcan XA903 was used for engine test work in support of the Concorde and Tornado programmes. (Marshall Aerospace plc)

Auster Aircraft Ltd continued to build military designs alongside their civilian products, the last military type being the AOP. Mk 9, which was first flown in 1954. (Author)

Re-structuring of the Industry

As the 1950s came to a close, it was clear that an industry in which every company built every type of aircraft could not be sustained. During this decade, all the manufacturers competed to develop and produce virtually every major class of aircraft, as indicated by the examples given in the table below:

Class of Aircraft	Manufacturers	Example Types
Bomber	A.V. Roe & Co. Ltd	Shackleton, Vulcan, Canberra (contract production)
	The English Electric Co. Ltd	Canberra
	Handley Page Ltd	Victor, Canberra (contract production)
	Vickers–Armstrongs Ltd	Valiant
	Short Brothers & Harland Ltd	Canberra (contract production)
Fighter	The de Havilland Aircraft Co. Ltd	Venom
	The English Electric Co. Ltd	Lightning
	Folland Aircraft Ltd	Gnat (export)
	The Gloster Aircraft Co. Ltd	Meteor, Javelin
Fighter	Hawker Aircraft Ltd	Hunter
	Vickers–Armstrongs Ltd	Swift, Scimitar
	Sir W.G. Armstrong Whitworth Aircraft Ltd	Hunter, Meteor and Javelin (contract production)
Military transport	Sir W.G. Armstrong Whitworth Aircraft Ltd	A.W.660 Argosy
	Blackburn & General Aircraft Ltd	Beverley
	The Bristol Aeroplane Co. Ltd	Freighter, Britannia

Class of Aircraft	Manufacturers	Example Types
	Handley Page Ltd	Hastings
	Vickers-Armstrongs Ltd	Valetta, Varsity
	Short Brothers & Harland Ltd (contract)	Britannia
Utility and communication	A.V. Roe & Co Ltd	Anson
	The de Havilland Aircraft Co. Ltd	Devon, Dove, Heron
	Hunting Percival Aircraft Ltd	Pembroke
	Scottish Aviation Ltd	Pioneer, Twin Pioneer
Trainer	The de Havilland Aircraft Co. Ltd	Vampire T.11, Chipmunk
	Folland Aircraft Ltd	Gnat T.1
	Hunting Percival Aircraft Ltd	Provost, Jet Provost
Naval aircraft	Sir W.G. Armstrong Whitworth Aircraft Ltd	Sea Hawk (contract production)
	Blackburn & General Aircraft Ltd	NA.39 Buccaneer
	The de Havilland Aircraft Co. Ltd	Sea Vixen
	The Fairey Aviation Co. Ltd	Gannet
	Hawker Aircraft Ltd	Sea Hawk
	Westland Aircraft Ltd	Wyvern

Sea Hawk assembly by Sir W.G. Armstrong Whitworth Aircraft Ltd, photographed in May 1953.
(Ray Williams archive)

The TSR.2 programme proved to be a major catalyst for the enforced rationalisation of the aircraft industry. (BAE SYSTEMS plc via Ken Ellis)

Class of Aircraft	Manufacturers	Example Types
Civil transport	Sir W.G. Armstrong Whitworth Aircraft Ltd	A.W.650 Argosy
	A.V. Roe & Co. Ltd	HS748 (first flew in 1960)
	The Bristol Aeroplane Co. Ltd	Britannia
	The de Havilland Aircraft Co. Ltd	Comet
	Handley Page Ltd	Herald
	Vickers-Armstrongs Ltd	Viscount, Vanguard
Helicopter	The Bristol Aeroplane Co. Ltd	Sycamore, Belvedere
	The Fairey Aviation Co. Ltd	Gyrodyne, Rotodyne (experimental types)
	Saunders-Roe Ltd	Skeeter
	Westland Aircraft Ltd	Sikorsky products and developments thereof
Private/Utility	Auster Aircraft Ltd	Extensive range
	Edgar Percival Aircraft Ltd	EP9 Prospector

With anything up to seven manufacturers competing for business to supply a single class of aircraft, the industry was looking at an unsustainable future. The Government recognised that this situation was unacceptable, and applied great pressure on the industry to produce rationalisation.

Duncan Sandys' 1957 Defence White Paper of 4 April 1957, *Outline of Future Policy*, has become somewhat notorious for its suggestion that missile technology was now maturing at such a rate that it would supplant the manned aircraft in many roles. It stated that in view of 'the good progress made towards the replacement of the manned aircraft of RAF Fighter Command with a ground to air missile system, the RAF are unlikely to have a requirement for fighter aircraft of types more advanced than the supersonic P.1, and work on such projects will stop'. Development of a supersonic manned bomber was not to be started, emphasis being switched to atomic weapons and guided missiles.

Clearly great changes in the aircraft industry were becoming inevitable. The first step was the formation of the British Aircraft Corporation Ltd in January 1960, the Government having indicated that it would only support the TSR.2 programme if it were to be produced by a single company. This resulted in the aviation interests of Vickers, Bristol and English Electric joining forces, with Hunting Aircraft following shortly afterwards. In parallel, the companies in the Hawker Siddeley Group – Armstrong Whitworth, A.V. Roe & Co. Ltd, Blackburn, Gloster and Hawker – found themselves being progressively joined by new bedfellows. These comprised Folland (in 1959); de Havilland and its Airspeed Division (in 1960); and Blackburn (also in 1960). In July 1963, this group was further reorganised to generate Hawker Siddeley Aviation Ltd.

Thus was created what *Aviation Week & Space Technology* has called the 'Society of Both Aircraft Companies'. This was something of an exaggeration as Short Brothers & Harland continued in Belfast, as did Scottish Aviation Ltd at Prestwick; Handley Page Ltd at Radlett; and Auster Aircraft Ltd at Rearsby. The helicopter industry was the subject of a similar Government-dictated rationalisation, in which Westland acquired the helicopter interests of its competitors: Saunders-Roe Ltd (in 1959); Bristol (in 1960); and Fairey Aviation (also in 1960).

6
Rationalisation: The BAC and Hawker Siddeley Years (1960–1977)

Market Trends – Commercial and General Aviation

BAC and Hawker Siddeley inherited a civil market that was struggling to break out from American domination. It is unfortunate that during the initial post-war period, a unique British ability to market the wrong products had resulted in the commercial market for piston-engined aircraft being dominated by the USA. It was doubly unfortunate then that despite the success of the Viscount, the Comet disasters opened the door to the Boeing 707 and DC-8.

If possible, worse was to follow. Myopic specifications from Britain's nationalised airlines (BEA and BOAC) and political indifference to the commercial aircraft industry undermined the potential of the Vanguard and VC10, BAC One-Eleven and Trident. The technically brilliant Concorde was economically, politically and environmentally flawed, particularly after the oil price shock of the 1970s, and the on-off-on development of the HS146 (later the BAe 146 and Avro RJ family) appeared to be driven by pure politics.

In a significant move for the future, the Hatfield Division of Hawker Siddeley entered into an agreement to develop wings for the new European consortium Airbus Industrie. This followed inter-governmental agreement to support Airbus project definition, signed in September 1967. From May 1969, the British government withdrew from further project funding, but Hawker Siddeley took the decision to continue in the project on a purely commercial basis.

The BAC One-Eleven was moderately successful in the commercial market with more than 230 aircraft sold. Two BAC One Eleven airliners are seen here in the bright sunshine of Las Vegas, having been withdrawn from service with US Air. (Author)

Concorde G-BOAD photographed at Heathrow in October 2003, during the type's final month of service with British Airways. (Author)

In the field of general aviation, the 1960s scene seemed more positive; Beagle (British Executive & General Aviation Ltd) was set up in October 1960, drawing upon the creative abilities of Auster at Rearsby, and F.G. Miles at Shoreham. New designs emerged in the shape of the Beagle Pup, the twin-engine Beagle 206, and the Bulldog military trainer. De Havilland had seen the value of the executive jet market and designed their DH125, initially known as the Jet Dragon, which was taken up and marketed by Hawker Siddeley as the HS125 with great success worldwide.

At Bembridge, Isle of Wight, John Britten and Desmond Norman had, through their operation of agricultural aircraft in some of the more basic areas of the world, identified the need for a simple robust utility aircraft capable of operation from short airstrips in all climates. The design that resulted – the Islander – fulfilled the designers' concept in every respect. On a larger scale, Shorts were also successful in bringing the utilitarian Skyvan into production for both civilian and military users.

In the helicopter arena, Westland Helicopters Ltd built a solid base from its manufacture of Sikorsky products under licence. The Whirlwind and Wessex attracted large-scale orders, and the Saunders-Roe P.531 was developed successfully into the Scout and Wasp. Westland boomed in the 1970s as the Anglo-French helicopter deal came to fruition, with WHL building its own Lynx, and the Aerospatiale-designed Puma and Gazelle. Simultaneously, the

The DH121 Trident was designed to meet the requirements of BEA and was eclipsed in terms of sales by Boeing's similarly configured Boeing 727. (Author)

The Beagle 206 and Pup briefly offered the potential for a British success in the General Aviation market. G-BSET, as its registration hints, was originally built for the RAF as the first production Beagle B206R Bassett CC.1. (Author)

Short's resolutely utilitarian Skyvan was produced for both civil and military customers. G-BLLI was exported to Aero Services of Barbados as 8P-ASG. (Bombardier Aerospace Belfast)

Royal Navy Lynx XZ727 approaches to land at RNAS Yeovilton. The type remains in production and continues to attract sales in export markets. (Author)

company secured large national and export orders for the Sea King helicopter, which it built under licence from Sikorsky in the USA.

Commercial Casualties

Handley Page Ltd, having achieved only modest sales with the HPR.7 Dart Herald, conceived a twin turboprop feeder liner, the Jetstream. The Jetstream was greeted with enormous enthusiasm in the marketplace, with significant sales achieved before its first flight. This sales success was in large measure dependent upon the aircraft delivering its declared performance, within its FAA certification limited maximum weight of 12,500lb. In the event, this could not be achieved.

Handley Page Ltd had invested in tools and facilities for large-scale production, and were now faced with a difficult and expensive development programme, whilst bearing the costs of their unfulfilled production expectations. The company proved unable to withstand the financial pressures and entered voluntary liquidation in August 1969, ceasing to trade in June 1970. The subsequent development of the aircraft by British Aerospace shows that this was, regrettably, another case of that British trait, most familiar in the field of sport, of defeat snatched from the jaws of victory.

Similar difficulties were encountered at Beagle. Here, despite the sale of nearly 400 Beagle Pup aircraft, the Government withdrew financial support to the company in December 1969. Beagle eventually produced 152 Pup aircraft and eighty-five Beagle 206. Even the hugely popular Islander suffered from the problems brought about by sales success. Although the aircraft survived and remains in limited production, the company suffered a series of financial crises, including a number of periods in receivership.

The SEPECAT Jaguar marked a move to international collaboration in the development of combat aircraft for the Royal Air Force that has continued to the present day. (Author)

Military Developments and Collaborative Ventures

In the military field, an almost mortal blow was struck when BAC, having been drawn together to produce the TSR.2, saw it cancelled by Dennis Healey in April 1965. BAC military efforts were then concentrated on the completion of Lightning production, supplemented by export Canberra refurbishment and the development of the pressurised Jet Provost T. Mk 5, and the BAC167 Strikemaster. BAC then moved on to the collaborative development of the Jaguar.

In the late 1960s, the RAF identified the requirement to reduce its number of front-line types, while achieving the following aims:

- The progressive replacement, from the late 1970s, of the Canberra and the V-bomber fleet.
- To establish the capability to carry out the low-level penetration roles that were to have been the province of the TSR.2.
- In the longer term, to phase out the Lightning and Phantom from their air defence roles.
- Also in the longer term, to replace the Buccaneer in its low-level strike, reconnaissance and maritime strike roles.

With all these objectives in mind, a further collaborative project emerged known as the Multi-Role Combat Aircraft, or MRCA – later named Tornado. BAC joined with MBB and Aeritalia to form Panavia to produce the Tornado, which first flew in 1974.

Recent successes in securing orders from the Royal Air Force and the Indian Air Force have confirmed the continued demand for the Hawk trainer. (Author)

Hawker Siddeley faced its own political traumas, with the cancellation of the supersonic V/STOL P.1154 project, the Royal Navy variant being cancelled by Peter Thorneycroft in February 1964. The RAF P.1154 version followed under the Healey axe of 1965, which also saw the cancellation of the HS.681 V/STOL transport. Despite these difficulties, Hawker Siddeley prospered on the strength of the products that it had inherited from its parent companies. Of particular note were the Harrier from Hawker, the HS.748 from A.V. Roe & Co. Ltd, and the HS125 from de Havilland. Other work included the Buccaneer (ex-Blackburn), the Nimrod maritime patrol aircraft, Hunter refurbishment, and production of the Trident.

During this period Hawker Siddeley designed what may prove to be Britain's last purely home-grown military aircraft, the HS.1182 Hawk trainer, which first flew in 1974, and continues to be one of the world's most successful trainer aircraft. In 1977, the next major stage in the development of the British Aircraft industry took place; the creation of British Aerospace – the 'Single British Aircraft Company'.

7
Modern Times

The Nationalisation and Privatisation of British Aerospace

British Aerospace (BAe) was formed as a nationalised corporation in April 1977, as a result of the Aircraft & Shipbuilding Industries Act 1977. In January 1981, BAe converted from a nationalised corporation to a public limited company (plc) in preparation for privatisation. The British Government sold 51.57 per cent of its shares in February 1981, and all but a single £1 'golden share' in May 1985. When BAe was founded, it employed some 50,000 people on eighteen sites – Bitteswell, Brough, Chadderton, Chester, Christchurch, Dunsfold, Filton, Hamble, Hatfield, Holme-on-Spalding Moor, Hurn, Kingston, Preston, Prestwick, Samlesbury, Warton, Weybridge and Woodford

Throughout its existence, BAe (now BAE SYSTEMS) has developed an ever more international flavour. The BAC collaboration on Jaguar was followed by the tri-national Tornado programme. Tornado production for Saudi Arabia has now ended, and BAE SYSTEMS has started production of Eurofighter, in partnership with Spain, Italy and Germany.

Something of a defining moment for the industry came on 24 December 1998 when new-build Sea Harrier FA.2 NB18 was 'bought off' by the Royal Navy customer. The completion of this aircraft was said by BAe to mark the last delivery of an all-British fighter aircraft to the UK armed services. One national programme, the Hawk, continues to go from strength to strength. Private venture developments of the Hawk 100 and Hawk 200 have allowed the type to remain effective, and it continues to be selected as the preferred training and light attack aircraft of many armed forces around the world. The latest order for the type was announced on 3 September 2003, the Indian Government procuring sixty-six Hawk aircraft for the Indian Air Force Advanced Jet Trainer programme.

Further ahead is the JSF programme, with BAE SYSTEMS teamed with Lockheed Martin to produce the supersonic CTOL/ASTOVL F-35 multi-role strike fighter for the USAF, US Navy, US Marine Corps and the RAF. Other transatlantic military co-operations include the T-45 Goshawk for the US Navy, and the AV-8B Harrier II and II Plus with McDonnell Douglas (now Boeing). Development work is underway on an extensively modified Nimrod, the MRA.4, (with new wings and engines) to preserve Britain's maritime patrol capability.

By the time of the merger of British Aerospace with Marconi Electronic Systems to form BAE SYSTEMS on 30 November 1999, the number of sites manufacturing aircraft components was down to eight – Brough, Chester, Chadderton, Filton, Prestwick, Samlesbury, Warton and Woodford – less than half the number of sites taken over in 1977.

BAe/BAE SYSTEMS Commercial Programmes

In the civil field, the establishment of the Airbus consortium has at last introduced a note of success into Britain's involvement in commercial aviation. Much against many observers' expectations, Airbus has proved to be a worthy rival to Boeing, achieving initial market penetration with the A300 and A310. These types have been followed up by the smaller, and hugely

Progressive development from the Short Skyvan resulted in the Short 330 and Short 360. These types have largely been superseded in airline use by pressurised turbo-props and regional jets. (Author)

successful, A320 family, and the A330 and A340 long-haul transports. Airbus has now launched its super-wide body project, the A380, and is also the nominated project management organisation for a joint European military transport project, the Future Large Aircraft A400M.

Elsewhere, the civil market has not proved a happy experience for British Aerospace/BAE SYSTEMS. Corporate jet activity was continued with production of the BAe125 (previously HS125, previously DH125). The aircraft has been extensively developed throughout its production life, the final BAe production versions being the Hawker 800 and Hawker 1000. BAe sold its corporate jet business to the Raytheon Corporation in June 1993.

BAe's regional turboprop products were the Jetstream and the Advanced Turbo-Prop, or ATP, a stretched and re-engined development of the Avro/HS.748. The ATP was manufactured at Woodford until October 1992, when production was transferred to Prestwick, and the aircraft re-launched under the designation Jetstream 61. At Prestwick, meanwhile, a growth version of the Jetstream, the Jetstream 41, was launched. Market conditions proved initially unfavourable due to production over-capacity in this sector. BAe responded by forming an alliance with Aerospatiale and Alenia known as Aero International (Regional), AI(R), with a view to rationalising product lines. An early casualty was the ATP/Jetstream 61, which, together with the original Jetstream 31, was not taken up by the AI(R) consortium. BAe continued with the Jetstream 41, but announced in May 1997 that the production line would close by the end of 1997. The AI(R) consortium was, itself, disbanded in 1998.

In the regional jet market, BAe produced the BAe 146, taken over from Hawker Siddeley. Although produced in significant numbers (219 aircraft), initially at Hatfield, and then at Woodford, the type was not a financial success for BAe. Production costs were high and many aircraft were leased on terms that ultimately proved unprofitable to BAe. The aircraft was re-launched as a family of types known as the Avro RJ (Regional Jet) series. Unfortunately, the terrorist attack on the New York World Trade Center on 11 September 2001 sounded the death knell for the RJ/RJX programme. On 27 November 2001, BAE SYSTEMS announced

The Cormorant is a long-range search and rescue version of the Utility variant of the EH101, which is operated by the Canadian Forces. This aircraft was displayed at the 2002 SBAC Show. (Author)

that it would be withdrawing from the construction of commercial aircraft at Woodford and would close the RJ and RJX programmes, with a consequential loss of 1,669 jobs. This decision, following the earlier suspension of the Jetstream 41 and 61 programmes at Prestwick, marked the end of BAE SYSTEMS construction of complete aircraft for the civil market.

The Wider Industry

Outside of BAe/BAE SYSTEMS, Shorts produced the SD330 and SD360 developments of their 'ugly-duckling' Skyvan, and went on to supply the RAF with an extensively developed version of the Embraer Tucano for basic training. The last SD360 was built in 1991, and the last Tucano in 1992. Purchased by Bombardier in 1989, the company has become increasingly centred upon aerospace component manufacture and assembly and it is unlikely that the company will ever build another complete aircraft.

The boom that Westland experienced in the late 1970s could not last. Partly as a result of its ill-starred WG30 civil helicopter venture, Westland found itself in financial difficulties in 1986. A huge political row erupted over whether WHL should accept a possible European rescue package, or one offered by Sikorsky. After much acrimony, including the resignation of Michael Heseltine from the cabinet, the Sikorsky option was taken.

Westland, like BAe, has taken an increasingly international route to secure its future. This has centred on the EH101 helicopter developed with Italy. WHL was purchased by GKN in 1994. During 1998, GKN announced its intention to combine its helicopter operations with those of the Italian company Agusta SpA. This merger has resulted in the formation of a new company, AgustaWestland, which has a mix of civil and military products, and involvement in both the EH101 and NH90 programmes. In the UK, the company has the EH101 and the WAH-64 Apache in production. The Lynx also remains in production, having gained new export success in the form of the Super Lynx 300. The helicopter marketplace worldwide still

More than 400 CFM Shadow aircraft have been built in a number of variants, which have been sold in thirty-six countries, the type being something of an unsung success of the industry. (Author)

features over-capacity, and AgustaWestland will continue to need good penetration in export markets to secure its long-term future. With EH101 export sales to Denmark, Portugal and Japan, and potential sales opportunities in the USA, helicopter production at Yeovil looks set to continue for some time to come. On 26 May 2004, GKN announced that it had agreed in principle to the sale of its 50 per cent shareholding in AgustaWestland to its Italian partner Finmeccanica. Britain's helicopter industry will become wholly Italian owned once this deal has been completed.

In the general aviation sector, the almost immortal Islander continues in limited production. Private aircraft have, for the most part, remained a bleak area for the British industry. Success has, however, been achieved by three products – the Slingsby T.67 Firefly, the CFM Shadow, and the Europa.

- Slingsby redesigned the Fournier RF6 (T.67A), adopting an all-composite structure and installing increased power to produce a highly successful fully aerobatic trainer, which has found favour at entry level with a number of air forces around the world.
- The CFM (Cook Flying Machines) Shadow was designed by David Cook of Leiston, Suffolk: more than 400 of these aircraft have been built in a number of variants, including the high performance Streak Shadow which flies at up to 105 knots on its 64hp. The Shadow and Streak Shadow have been sold in more than thirty-six countries, and have completed many notable flights, including from England to Australia. As with so many British aircraft manufacturers there have been trading difficulties along the way. CFM Metal Fax Ltd went into liquidation in November 1996 and was taken over by CFM Aircraft Ltd in 1997. CFM Aircraft Ltd was, itself, in receivership in autumn 2002, before being taken over by CFM Airborne Inc. of Texas who announced in November 2002 the setting up of a UK facility: CFM Airborne (UK) Ltd.
- Ivan Shaw's all-composite Europa, designed for the home-built and kit construction market, first flew in September 1992. The aircraft was built by The Europa Aircraft Co., which after a management buy-out became Europa Management (International)

Ltd on 1 August 2001. On 24 November 2003, Europa Management (International) Ltd announced that the total number of kits sold had passed the significant total of 1,000 in thirty-four countries.

Future Prospects

Where does the future of the British industry lie? Shrinking defence markets have forced rationalisation in the USA. To some extent, this was also the engine for the creation of Hawker Siddeley and BAC, and subsequently the formation of British Aerospace and BAE SYSTEMS. With an increasing trend toward collaborative projects, and the large-scale of investment required to launch new projects, aerospace is rapidly moving towards being a global business.

Lockheed, Martin Marietta, General Dynamics (Fort Worth Division), IBM, Loral, and Vought have already coalesced into a single corporation. Northrop and Grumman have merged to become Northrop Grumman, and Boeing has absorbed the earlier combine of McDonnell and Douglas. Faced with these giant businesses, European re-structuring has become inevitable. British Aerospace took a 35 per cent share in Saab of Sweden and spent a period in ultimately unsuccessful restructuring discussions with DaimlerChrysler Aerospace of Germany (DASA).

On 19 January 1999, BAe and GEC announced that they had reached agreement on the merger of BAe with the GEC defence interests (Marconi Electronic Systems). This merger, effective from the end of November 1999, created BAE SYSTEMS, then Europe's largest defence company, ranking at third largest in the world with a workforce of nearly 100,000 employees. In response to the creation of BAE SYSTEMS, DaimlerChrysler announced in June 1999 that they were acquiring the Spanish company CASA, thereby strengthening their position for future restructuring discussions. An agreement with Aerospatiale Matra followed, leading to the formation of EADS (European Aeronautic Defence & Space Co.), on 10 July 2000. EADS is the world's third largest defence organisation, behind Boeing and Lockheed Martin, displacing BAE SYSTEMS from this position.

With transatlantic projects such as JSF looking to secure global export markets, overtures from the major players in the USA may not be long delayed. A future global aerospace business may yet be created by one of the major US defence conglomerates acting in partnership with BAE SYSTEMS and/or EADS. Over recent years, the press has at various times linked BAE SYSTEMS with overtures from Lockheed Martin, Boeing and General Dynamics. In ten years' time, it is hard to believe that the current structure of the industry will not have seen further upheaval – we will have to wait and see. By that time, indeed, it may seem almost quaint to refer to the British Aircraft Industry.

8
The Genealogy of British Aerospace/BAE SYSTEMS

The preceding narrative has charted the evolution of the British aircraft industry. Much of the manufacturing capacity of the industry is now in the hands of only two companies: BAE SYSTEMS (previously British Aerospace plc), manufacturing military fixed-wing aircraft and commercial aircraft components, and AgustaWestland (previously GKN Westland Helicopters Ltd), manufacturing military helicopters in the UK.

The narrative has shown how political and commercial imperatives led to progressive re-structuring of the industry. The impact of these changes is best appreciated when presented in the form of a family tree. BAE SYSTEMS came into being with the merger between British Aerospace and the defence interests of GEC, Marconi Electronic Systems (MES). As MES did not include any UK aircraft manufacturers in its heritage, the following family tree represents only the British Aerospace heritage that passed into BAE SYSTEMS. Three diagrams are presented:

1 British Aerospace: The Big Picture
2 BAe: Hawker Siddeley Companies
3 BAe: British Aircraft Corporation and Scottish Aviation

Whilst in many respects, these diagrams speak for themselves, a few observations are worth making:

- British Aerospace was formed in 1977 by the merging of three companies: Hawker Siddeley Aviation Ltd, the British Aircraft Corporation (BAC) and Scottish Aviation Ltd. Short Brothers & Harland were the only major fixed-wing aircraft manufacturer that remained independent of this group.
- Because Scottish Aviation Ltd had acquired the rump of the Beagle Aircraft Ltd and Handley Page Ltd activities, they effectively brought with them into the BAe family tree the heritage of these firms. This encompasses (via Handley Page Ltd) Martinsyde Ltd and Phillips & Powis/Miles Aircraft Ltd, and (via Beagle) Auster Aircaft Ltd and Taylorcraft Aeroplanes (England) Ltd.
- Hawker Siddeley Aviation Ltd (HSAL) added Blackburn and General Aircraft Ltd, the de Havilland Aircraft Co. Ltd and Folland Aircraft Ltd to the group of Hawker Siddeley companies which had already been merged in 1935, although continuing to trade under their original identities (A.V. Roe & Co. Ltd, Hawker Aircraft Ltd, Gloster Aircraft Company Ltd, and Sir W.G. Armstrong Whitworth Aircraft Ltd).
- The less familiar antecedents of HSAL include H.H. Martyn & Co. (via Gloster), William Denny & Bros Ltd, General Aircraft Ltd and CWA Ltd (via Blackburn) and Airspeed Ltd, May Harden & May and Wycombe Aircraft Constructors (via AIRCO/de Havilland).
- Only four companies were grouped into BAC, these being English Electric Aviation Ltd, Bristol Aircraft Ltd (previously the Bristol Aeroplane Co. Ltd), Vickers-

Armstrongs (Aircraft) Ltd and Hunting Aircraft Ltd (previously Percival Aircraft Ltd). The Vickers–Armstrongs heritage includes The Supermarine Aviation Works Ltd and Pemberton-Billing Ltd. The aircraft interests of The English Electric Co. Ltd were originally formed by merging the aircraft activities of Coventry Ordnance Works, Phoenix Dynamo Co. Ltd and Dick, Kerr & Co. in December 1918.

- Between 1919 and 1921 many company names were changed, and a number of new companies were founded following the closure of closely linked predecessors. This reflects the impact of taxation imposed after the First World War on companies that were considered to have made excess profits.

BAe: The Big Picture

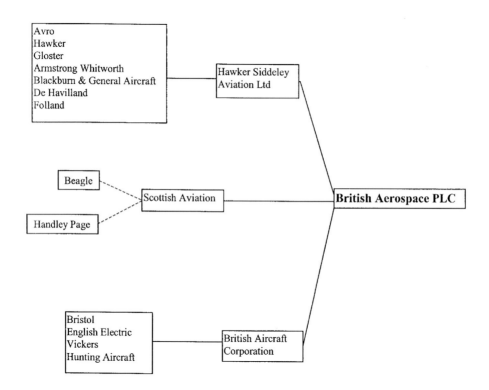

British Aerospace - Hawker Siddeley Companies

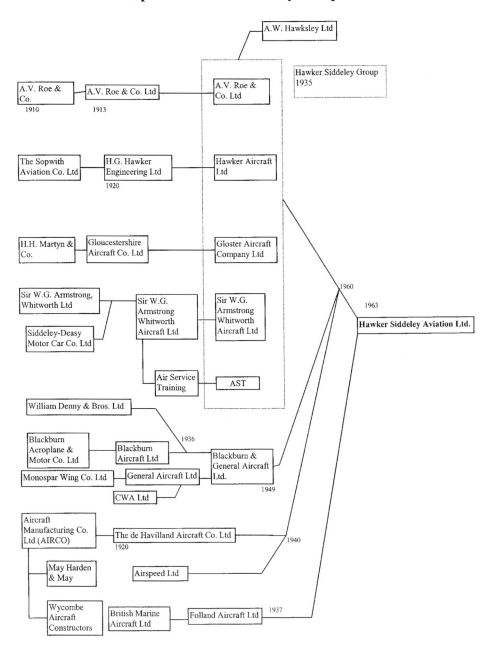

BAe: British Aircraft Corporation & Scottish Aviation

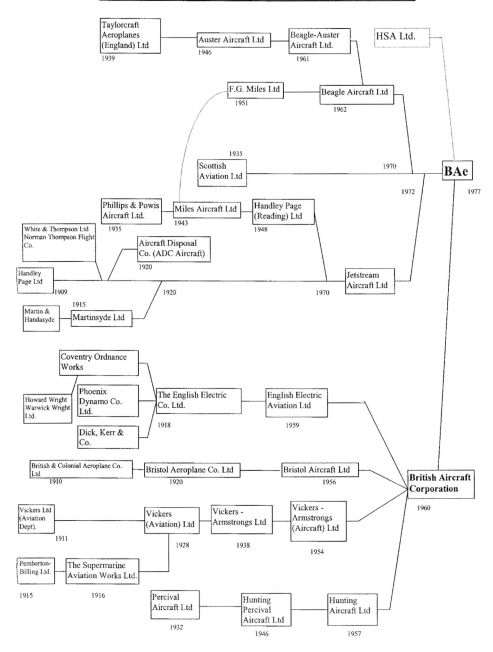

The Aircraft Manufacturers of Central & Eastern England

Bedfordshire

Barton le Clay (disused arfield west of Luton)

Luton Aircraft Ltd: This company operated at Barton le Clay from July 1935, having briefly been styled the Dunstable Aircraft Co. Luton Aircraft Ltd was registered on 4 November 1935. The Luton LA.1 Buzzard, G-ADYX first flew at Barton le Clay in mid-1936. The Buzzard was a single-seat low-wing monoplane with a pylon-mounted pusher engine, which was reported as having excellent handling and a superb view, but a rather poor climb rate. The Buzzard was propelled by a V-twin Anzani 'of Morgan three-wheeler ancestry', which proved to be unreliable. The Buzzard was re-built with a number of modifications as the Buzzard II, following a crash in November 1936. The Buzzard II emerged in the spring of 1938, with a much cleaner nacelle and engine installation, closed cockpit, and reduced wingspan.

The Luton LA.2 tandem-wing aircraft (whose fuselage was used by the later LA.3 Minor) was tested at Barton le Clay in late 1936, but proved reluctant to fly. In February 1936, the company was advertising: 'Flying Flea £165; complete set of materials £25. All components and materials stocked.'

The Luton LA.1 Buzzard, seen in its initial form at Barton le Clay in 1936. (Military Aircraft Photographs)

Later products were constructed at the Phoenix Works, Gerrards Cross, Buckinghamshire, particularly the outstandingly successful Luton Minor, which has become very popular as a home-built aircraft. The company moved to Gerrards Cross in September 1936. C.H. Latimer-Needham was the designer of both the Luton Buzzard and Luton Minor, and is also associated with the Halton Mayfly (G-EBOO), Martin Monoplane (G-AEYY), and the Dunstable Sailplane Co.

D.M.K. Marendaz Ltd/Marendaz Special Cars Ltd set up a company in 1937 known as **International Aircraft & Engineering Ltd**, at Cordwallis Works, Maidenhead with a view to entering the aircraft industry. Unfortunately, the works were destroyed by fire in June 1937. By October 1937, the firm was active at Barton le Clay, where Captain Marendaz was the owner of the Bedford School of Flying.

The first Marendaz design was the Marendaz Special Monoplane, described in *The Aeroplane* of February 1936. A general arrangement drawing showed this to be a two-seat side-by-side low-wing cabin monoplane with a fixed spatted undercarriage and a Pobjoy engine. The type had rectangular wings of 28ft span, with a tip shape that was cut back to give a reduced length to the trailing edge compared with the leading edge. The standard version was to feature wire braced wings, with a full cantilever version available at extra cost. In overall configuration the type resembled a rectangular wing version of the Aeronca LB or Ryan SCW.

The Aeroplane commented that 'the company are known as makers of custom-built sports cars that are comfortable to drive and easy to handle'. Ord-Hume reports that the Marendaz Special Monoplane was not proceeded with solely because Captain Marendaz neglected to acknowledge the role of G.N. Wikner in the design of the aircraft when it was initially publicised.

The second type to be built was the Marendaz III retractable undercarriage low-wing cabin monoplane. The first prototype was destroyed as a result of the fire at the Cordwallis Works, but the type nevertheless emerged in the form of G-AFGG, which was displayed (statically) at the Royal Aeronautical Society Garden Party at Harmondsworth in May 1938. G-AFGG was built at Barton le Clay, in the same works as were used by Luton Aircraft Ltd, and is widely believed never to have flown, although there is no conclusive evidence in this regard.

International Aircraft & Engineering entered receivership in June 1938, following which a further company, **Marendaz Aircraft Ltd**, was established. This company constructed a Cirrus Minor-powered, low-wing, tandem two-seat, open-cockpit aircraft, the Marendaz Trainer – G-AFZX – which was briefly flown in late 1939 before being presented to the local Air Training Corps Squadron at Halton.

Barton le Clay airfield was used by the Air Transport Auxiliary as an initial flying training unit from the summer of 1942.

Bedford area

W.H. Allen, Sons & Co. Ltd, of Queen's Engineering Works, Bedford was a manufacturer of aero engines during the First World War, including the 110hp Le Rhône rotary, and the proud possessor of the telephone number No.1, Bedford.

Some significant first flights were made at **Royal Aircraft Establishment Bedford**. Most types that made their first flights at RAE Bedford were experimental or prototype aircraft as indicated in the following table:

The world's slenderest delta, this research aircraft, the H.P.115, is investigating the low-speed handling properties of a supersonic-airliner planform.

The slender delta wing of the HP115 provided low-speed test data in support of the Concorde programme. The type made its first flight at RAE Bedford in August 1961. (Handley Page Association)

Type	Serial or Registration	Date	Comments
Blackburn NA.39	XK486	30 April 1958	Prototype: developed into Buccaneer.
P.1127	XP831	13 March 1961	First conventional flight. developed via Kestrel into Harrier.
Handley Page 115	XP841	17 August 1961	Low-speed aerodynamics and control research in support of Concorde.
Bristol 188	XF923	14 April 1962	High-speed research aircraft.
Hunting 126	XN714	26 March 1963	Jet-flap research aircraft, additional comments below.
CMC Leopard	G-BKRL	12 December 1988	Personal jet aircraft developed by Chichester Miles Consultants Ltd.

The Short SB5, built to investigate the low-speed characteristics of highly swept wings in support of the English Electric P.1 programme, was based at RAE Bedford. It was flown for the first time in its maximum wing sweep configuration (69 degrees) on 10 October 1960. The Hunting 126 succeeded in demonstrating previously unheralded in-flight lift coefficients, but also demonstrated violent and unpredictable post-stall characteristics. The Short SC1, the first United Kingdom jet VTOL aircraft to make a full transition between hovering and vertical flight, was also operated at RAE Bedford. Two were built, XG900 and XG905, the first full transition being flown by XG905 on 6 April 1960. Both aircraft continued to operate at RAE Bedford until 1971.

Short Brothers (Rochester & Bedford) Ltd manufactured and tested balloons and airships at Cardington, south east of Bedford, before this facility was taken over by the Government.

Skysport Engineering Ltd, of Rotary Farm, Thorncote Green, Sandy, close to Old Warden, are noted for their restoration projects, and have also built reproductions to 'as new' standard. The following examples give an indication of the challenging restorations and reproductions for which Skysport has become well known:

Type	Registration	Comments
Avro Avian	VH-UFZ	Accident repair 1998.
BE2C	2699	Refurbished for The Imperial War Museum in 1989.
BE2E	A1325/G-BVGR	Under restoration for the Mosquito Aircraft Museum in 1994, subsequently moved to AJD Engineering.
Blériot XI	G-AVXE	Refurbished in 1989 for a cross-channel flight to celebrate the 80th anniversary of Blériot's original crossing. Regrettably, the flight was unsuccessful, ending in the sea on 25 July 1989. The ditching led to a second Skysport restoration, which was completed in 1992.
Bristol Beaufighter IF	G-DINT/ X7688	Under rebuild.
Bristol F.2B Fighter	G-ACAA/ 'D8084'	Restored for The Fighter Collection at Duxford, and structurally complete by September 1992, but awaiting engine work. First flown at Old Warden on 30 June 1998.
Bristol F.2B Fighter	E2581	Renovation for the Imperial War Museum.
Bristol F.2B Fighter	Be/66	Restored for the Brussels Military Museum.
Bucker Jungmann	G-AZNG	Overhaul.
Bulldog IIA	G-ABBB/ 'K2227'	This aircraft was the last airworthy Bristol Bulldog. It was originally restored to flying condition by its manufacturers, flying on 22 June 1961. Unfortunately, it was severely

The Hunting H.126 XN714 was used for jet flap research, this being based on the use of a high-speed jet efflux from the wing trailing edge providing both increased lift and propulsion. (BAE SYSTEMS plc via Ken Ellis)

Type	Registration	Comments
		damaged in a major accident at Farnborough on 13 September 1964. Skysport have undertaken a painstaking rebuild of the shattered wreckage, with the two remaining fuselage sections re-joined using newly built structure. Following its rebuild, the restored machine was put on display at the RAF Museum, Hendon.
Comper Swift	G-ABUU	To Spain after overhaul.
DH Tiger Moth work		G-AKUE 1988, G-ANOR (repair), G-AOEI (part restoration), G-APLU (repair), G-APIH (repair), G-BTYN (current restoration).
DH84 Dragon	G-ACIT	Restoration to airworthy condition for Science Museum, Wroughton.
Fieseler Storch	G-FIST	Part restoration, to Italy.
Hawker Demon	K8203/G-BTVE	Under rebuild in 1994 and continues.
Hawker Fury replica	G-BKBB	Rebuild after accident, test-flown January 2001.
Miles Falcon	EC-ACB	Airframe restoration work.
Miles Falcon	G-AEEG	Overhaul.
Miles Gemini	G-AKEK	Current project (major restoration).
Miles Messenger	G-AJWB	Restoration, first flight 19 December 2001.

G-EAGA is one of the fine replicas and restorations completed by Skysport Ltd. (Author)

Type	Registration	Comments
Nieuport 28	G-BSKS	Rebuilt aircraft, first test-flown from Henlow on 6 May 1991 and delivered to the US Army Aviation Museum at Fort Rucker, Alabama, after a short, but apparently incredibly noisy, flying career.
Percival Mew Gull	G-AEXF	Rebuild post-accident 1991.
Sopwith Camel	N6812	Renovation for the Imperial War Museum.
Sopwith Dove	G-EAGA	Superlative reproduction flown for the first time at Henlow on 28 March 1993.
Sopwith Pup replica	G-BIAT/N6160	Crashed at Old Warden on its first flight on 2 July 1986. Restored and displayed at RNZAF Museum.
Sopwith Pup replica	G-BIAU	Airworthy at FAA Museum, Yeovilton. Built 1980–86.
Stampe work		G-ANXW (overhaul), G-AXRP (underway), G-AYZI (part restoration), G-AZNK, G-BHYI, G-BLOL (underway), G-FORC (overhaul), G-FORD (new fuselage completed March 1997), G-SVIV.
Thruxton Jackaroo	G-ANZT	Restoration, first flight September 1996.
Tipsy Belfair	G-APIE	Overhaul.
Valmet Viima	OO-EBL	Total rebuild completed mid-1994.
Westland Wallace	K6035	Restoration began in the mid-1980s for the RAF Museum, and took seven years to complete, finishing in 1993.

Work on more modern types has included the overhaul (part restoration) of Chipmunks G-ARGG and G-BBND, and and renovation of Cessna 150 G-AWAW for the Science Museum. Skysport has also worked on a wide range of other artifacts, aircraft engines and other items for museum display purposes.

Cranfield

Cranfield College of Aeronautics/Cranfield Institute Technology/Cranfield University: The College of Aeronautics carried out laminar flow and other aerofoil research using Lancaster I PA474 (now the star of the RAF Battle of Britain Memorial Flight). In 1957 the College of Aeronautics began using the Short SB4 Sherpa as an experimental aircraft, marked G-36-1.

Engineering work by the College of Aeronautics included the conversion of Smiths Aviation Division Varsity G-ARFP/WF387 for autoland research. **Cranfield Engineering** holds CAA Airworthiness approval, and has been involved (with Cranfield Aeronautical Services Ltd) in a number of experimental aircraft programmes for the MoD, including the variable stability Beagle 206 and Hawk aircraft, and the advanced control VAAC Harrier T.2. Cranfield Engineering also operated specialist facilities for wet runway water ingestion trials and developed a 2,000 US gallon capacity water bomber conversion of the HS.748. This aircraft, known as the Macavia Turbine Tanker was first flown on 4 September 1987.

In 2002, it was announced by BAE SYSTEMS that it had sold a BAe 146-200 design data pack to **Cranfield Aerospace Ltd** to allow them to design a new freighter variant of the type for TRONOS plc (a specialist lessor of BAe 146 aircraft). The work is being conducted jointly between Cranfield Aerospace Ltd and Hireplane Cargo Conversions Ltd (a TRONOS

The airfield and college at Cranfield are seen here bathed in the light of a summer evening in 1994. (Author)

This conversion of the HS748 to the Macavia Turbine Tanker water bomber is representative of the work of Cranfield Engineering. (Author)

G-COAI is the Cranfield A1 modified to two-seat configuration as the Cranfield A1-200. (J.S. Smith)

The prototype of the insect-like Edgeley Optica was flown at Cranfield in 1979. This is a production aircraft being displayed at a Farnborough SBAC Show. (Author)

subsidiary). The type would have an 11-tonne payload capacity without floor strengthening, and up to 12.6 tonnes capacity with floor strengthening. A large freight door has been incorporated, measuring 96 by 76 inches. In mid-2003, it was expected that the first converted aircraft would be available in January 2004.

Flight Invert Ltd was set up by Cranfield University and provides the design authority for the Cranfield A.1 aerobatic aircraft, the sole example of which (G-BCIT) first flew on 23 August 1976. This aircraft, whilst a successful design project, proved not to be a fully competitive aerobatic mount. This was due in part to some deficiencies in handling, notably an unwillingness to flick roll cleanly.

A follow-on project, completed in 1998, was the conversion of the aircraft to two-seat configuration, this being accompanied by a number of modifications to improve performance. The aircraft is now designated Cranfield A.1-200 and carries the registration G-COAI.

The **CMC** (Chichester Miles Consultants Ltd) Leopard prototype G-BKRL was at Cranfield for a lengthy period prior to its first flight at RAE Bedford. Cranfield was also used as flight test base for the second aircraft G-BRNM.

The **Edgley Aircraft Co. Ltd** Optica prototype G-BGMW first flew at Cranfield on 14 December 1979. (Development and production of the type was subsequently continued at Old Sarum and Hurn.)

Handley Page Ltd: The Victor prototype was tested here during speed measurement trials following complaints about noise from the residents of Radlett. This testing was curtailed by the crash of the prototype in July 1954.

The diminutive Volkswagen-powered Plumb BGP-1 is seen here at Compton Abbas. First registered in 1978, its immaculate appearance belies its age. (Author)

The **Manuel** Hawk glider first flew at Cranfield in November 1972, having been constructed at Fairoaks.

The **Plumb** BGP.1 is an original single-seat design built by Barry Plumb, having its origins in a PFA design competition. The sole aircraft (G-BGPI) was built by its designer, and has been flying successfully for many years.

Dunstable

From 1934, **Zander & Weyl**, of Luton Road, Dunstable, built primary gliders, and replica gliders for film use, followed by a Flying Flea G-ADSE. The company name was changed to **Dart Aircraft Ltd**, on 11 March 1936, the office address changing to 29 High Street North, Dunstable.

The Dart Pup, originally named the Dunstable Dart, was a pusher parasol monoplane, similar to a single-seat Shackleton-Murray SM.1, except for its sweptback wing planform, which resembled that of the Slingsby Falcon glider. Registered G-AELR, the Dart flew in July or August 1936. The completely unobstructed cockpit must have provided an exceptional field of view for the pilot. After trial assembly of the aircraft at High Street North, test-flying was carried out at two local farms – Blow's Farm and Loosey Farm.

The next design, the Dart Flittermouse, G-AELZ, flew at the end of August 1936 and was subsequently based at Witney. This was an inelegant high-wing pusher design with a single-seat fuselage pod for the pilot, and a space frame rear fuselage, in some ways reminiscent of the modern Mike Whittaker series of pod and boom microlight aircraft.

The Dart Kitten was, by contrast, a delightful single-seat low-wing monoplane. The proto-type, G-AERP, first flew on 15 January 1937. Originally powered by a 24hp two-stroke Ava engine, the aircraft suffered from high vibration when gliding. When fitted with a 36hp JAP, the Dart Kitten II G-AEXT achieved 1.5gph at 75mph, a remarkable performance. In June 1937, the advertising ran: 'The plane without vices. Price from £345. Dart Aircraft Ltd, Dunstable.'

An unfulfilled project was the Dart Weasel of 1939, which resembled a tricycle undercarriage version of the Moth Minor. The construction of the **Handley Page Manx** was subcontracted to Dart Aircraft Ltd in 1938-39, although the aircraft did not fly until 1943, completion of this complex project proving beyond the resources of the company. Mr Weyl built an additional Dart Kitten G-AMJP, styled the Dart Kitten III, in 1951. A home-built Kitten VH-WGL was also registered in New Guinea in 1960.

A further involvement of Mr Zander with aviation was with the 1937 firm of **Zander & Scott Ltd**, 32 Lovers Walk, Dunstable, which was re-named **Scott Light Aircraft Ltd** on 5 December 1938, with offices at 27 Albion Street, Dunstable. This company's main product was the Hutter 17 glider, for which Scott had obtained the UK rights, and the Viking sailplane. The Viking 2 was used during the Second World War for radar trials from Christchurch. The company was reformed as **Scott Aero Precision Ltd** and made jigs and fixtures for the aircraft industry during the Second World War.

Subsequently, Mr Zander was involved in the **Hawkridge Aircraft Co.**, which was formed in 1945 with works at High Street Dunstable, and built about sixteen gliders including the Venture and Kittiwake.

The **Dunstable Sailplane Co.** was formed by C.H. Latimer-Needham in 1935, with W.L. Manuel, another well-known sailplane designer as Manager. The company later amalgamated with Latimer-Needham's **Luton Aircraft Co.** to form **Phoenix Aircraft Ltd**, with offices at Cranleigh, Surrey.

The long-winged Dart Kitten shows off its clean and elegant lines at the fly-in to celebrate Shoreham's sixty years as a municipal airport. (Author)

Henlow (near Bedford)

Although not a manufacturing site as such, the RAF Maintenance Unit at Henlow erected and test-flew 1,004 Canadian-built Hurricanes between June 1940 and October 1943. It was also responsible for the overhaul, repair and modification of a large number of Hurricane, Blenheim, Hampden, Halifax, Tomahawk, Hudson, Mosquito, Typhoon and Tempest aircraft.

The site was later used as the restoration facility for the RAF Museum, doing superlative, painstaking work on a number of historic aircraft, before this activity moved to nearby Cardington in 1974.

Henlow has also been used by **Skysport Ltd** for flight testing of their restored and replica aircraft. Skysport aircraft flown here include Nieuport 28, G–BSKS on 6 May 1991, and Sopwith Dove G–EAGA on 28 March 1993.

Leighton Buzzard

Morgan & Co. Ltd, of Linslade – close to the site of the 1960s 'Great Train Robbery' – built a significant number of aircraft during the First World War. Barry Abraham (private communication) indicates that the origins of the company were as a coachworks, later building car bodies for other manufacturers. At the start of the First World War, they constructed corrugated iron sheds before turning to aircraft construction. The factory was situated on Canal Road (now Leighton Road), between the canal and the river. Vimy Road (previously Vimy Lane) runs next to the site of the Morgan & Co. works, which were taken over in 1934 by Foundry Equipment Ltd.

Aircraft were taken without wings to Scotts field on the Billington Road for erection and flying. A variety of types were manufactured, including the Avro 504K (150 ordered on 26 February 1918, delivered by 25 January 1919), AIRCO DH6 (200), Vickers Vimy (forty-two built from an order for fifty), and Sopwith 1½ Strutter (seventy-one of 200 ordered, although some sources state approximately 100 of 200). The company had London offices at 10 Old Bond Street, London W1.

Luton

Hewlett & Blondeau Ltd, Oak Road, Leagrave, Luton, 'Telegraphic address 'Aeromnia'. This company originated with the Hewlett & Blondeau School at Brooklands. The school began manufacturing aircraft and established a factory at Battersea in a disused skating rink. The company moved to a purpose built works at Leagrave near Luton due to rapidly increasing production demand. Mrs Hewlett was the senior partner of the company and was a very striking woman (to judge from the photograph published in *The Aeroplane*, on 24 October 1917).

The main type built by Hewlett & Blondeau at Luton was the Armstrong Whitworth FK3 of which 350 were ordered, with the first contract being placed in June 1916; at least 225 FK3 were completed. Other types included BE2C (forty aircraft, some built at Battersea), Blackburn AD Scout (two), Avro 504K, and the Dyott Bomber. The Dyott Bomber was a large Vimy-like twin-engine aircraft with a tricycle undercarriage, constructed in only three months. The company built no less than 400 Avro 504J/K.

The site at Leagrave (between Luton and Dunstable) was an undeveloped cornfield when it was chosen in May 1914, with production being underway by the autumn. By May 1915, BE2C were being built here. Ten types of aircraft were built at Battersea (including Hanriot, Caudron and Dyott) before the move to Leagrave. The new site was equipped to build complete aeroplanes, taking in only raw material – all required processes, components and details being completed on site.

Hewlett & Blondeau Ltd at Leagrave was a major contractor for the Armstrong Whitworth FK3. (Ray Williams)

D7103 is one of some 400 Avro 504J/K built by Hewlett & Blondeau Ltd. (BAE SYSTEMS plc)

D. Napier & Son Ltd engine testing: The Napier Experimental Engine Installation Unit moved to Luton Airport from Northolt in 1940. A summary of engine test bed aircraft operated in support of Napier is given below (not all these aircraft necessarily operated from Luton, however):

Engine Type	Test bed Fleet
Dagger	Hawker Hart K2434, which first flew at Brooklands on 17 November 1933 with a Dagger I, was subsequently used to test the Dagger II and III. This aircraft was, in effect, a precursor to the Hawker Hector and remained active for some five years. A photograph of K2434 at Luton in 1938 is included in F.K. Mason's *Hawker Aircraft Since 1920*. Fairey Battle K9240 was used as a test bed for the Dagger VIII.
Sabre	From 1940, a series of aircraft, mainly Hawker Typhoon and Tempest, were based at Luton in support of Sabre development. The test fleet was known as the Napier Squadron. Fairey Battle L5286, Vickers Warwick CIII HG248 (fitted with Sabre VI engines), and two Folland 43/37 specialist flying test bed aircraft were also used in this effort. Typhoon aircraft used included R8694 for annular radiator trials, R7712, R7651, R7771 which was used for Sabre IIA radiator trials and R8803. Tempest V NV768 was fitted with a Sabre engine and used for annular radiator trials (looking very like a Tempest II), and Tempest VI NX116 was also allocated to Napier trials.
Nomad	Avro Lincoln SX973 tested this engine in 1953, followed by Shackleton VW131.
Naiad	Avro Lincoln RF402, RF530. RF402/G-APRP served Napier & Son from 1948 until 1957, initially on Naiad intake icing research, and subsequently, on more general icing research.
Eland	The second prototype Vickers Varsity VX835, flown in mid-1954; Airspeed Ambassador G-ALFR, 1955.
Phoebus	Avro Lincoln RA643 – installation work by D. Napier & Son at Luton in 1947, test-flying from Filton.

The second prototype Varsity VX835 was used as a test bed for the Napier Eland engine. It is seen here with an icing test spray rig positioned in front of the starboard engine. (Brooklands Museum Trust)

The fine lines of the Percival Q.6 are evident in this photograph of three of the type flying in formation. The post-war de Havilland Dove successfully met much the same requirement. (Percival Aircraft Ltd via Ken Ellis)

Engine Type	Test bed Fleet
Avon, Conway, Sapphire	Avro Ashton Mk 2 WB491 converted for engine testing by D. Napier & Son at Luton in 1954. Ashton Mk 3 WE670 was similarly modified for engine icing tests at Luton.
Scorpion rocket motor	English Electric Canberra WK163. The Napier Double Scorpion Canberra set an altitude record of 70,310ft on 28 August 1957.

In addition to the above aircraft on engine test duty, Napier used a number of aircraft for icing research, including Avro Lincoln RF402/G-APRP and G-29-1/RF342/G-APRJ/G-36-3, and Fairey Spearfish RA356.

Percival Aircraft Ltd moved to Luton from Gravesend in October 1936. The main products of Percival Aircraft were their own designs: the P.3 Gull, P.6 Mew Gull, and P.10 Vega Gull (G-AEAB first flown at Gravesend in November 1935, ninety built); the Q.6 (prototype X-1/G-AEYE first flown on 14 September 1937, twenty-seven built); and the Proctor. The Percival Q.6 Petrel was an elegant twin-engine machine, designed to much the same requirement as the later de Havilland Dove.

Post-war construction included the Merganser and Prince twin-engine aircraft, and the Prentice and Provost trainers. These latter aircraft were subject to further development after the company changed its name to **Hunting Percival Aircraft Ltd** in 1954.

*PF606 was built by Percival Aircraft Ltd as a PR.XXXIV, and subsequently converted to a Mosquito TT.39.
(BAE SYSTEMS plc)*

A75.1 is a Royal Australian Air Force Proctor, preserved at Moorabbin, Victoria, Australia. (Author)

During the Second World War, Percival undertook contract production of the Airspeed Oxford (a total of 1,525 being built, although 1,360 and 1,356 are also quoted) and the de Havilland Mosquito (245 B. XVI and PR.34). 1,142 Proctor communications aircraft were produced for military service, the type being first flown (P5998) at Luton on 8 October 1939. F. Hills & Sons of Manchester built 812 of these Proctor aircraft. Total Proctor production, including 154 P.44 Proctor V built specifically for civil use, was 1,296 aircraft.

The success of the Proctor is reflected in the following advertisement for the Proctor V, published in April 1948: 'The most popular British Light Aircraft in the World today', and listing its countries of operation as Iceland, Canada, USA, New Zealand, Chile, Brazil, Argentina, Sweden, Denmark, Netherlands, Belgium, France, Portugal, Algeria, Syria, Great Britain, Iraq, Egypt, India, Kenya, Belgian Congo, Northern and Southern Rhodesia, Australia and South Africa.

After the end of the Second World War, Percival built a single prototype of a small high-wing twin-engine transport, the Merganser. The Merganser flew for the first time on 16 May 1947 bearing the registration X-2, later G-AHMH. Contemporary advertising indicates some of the Merganser's main features:

> 6ft headroom in a 5/8 seat airliner. An all metal 5/8 seater monoplane with tricycle under-carriage. Equally suitable as an airliner, for charter or hire, luxury private travel, as a freighter or an ambulance. Unobstructed view of the ground from all seats. Cabin bulkheads, panelling and fittings easily removed and replaced...

Post-war production centred on the Prentice; the Prince and its derivatives; the Provost; and the Jet Provost. A total of 432 P.40 Prentice training aircraft were built, the prototype TV163 being flown for the first time on 31 March 1946. Designed against RAF specification T.23/43, the type was also sold to Argentina and the Lebanon, and built under licence in India. Blackburn Aircraft Ltd built 125 Prentice at Brough.

The Prince was a twin-engine light transport that led to a family of military communication and training aircraft for the Royal Navy (Sea Prince) and Royal Air Force (Pembroke). Although bearing a strong family resemblance to the Merganser, the Prince was larger and heavier, with 8ft longer wing span, nearly double the weight and almost twice the installed power. The Sea Prince for the Royal Navy was first flown on 28 June 1951. The prototype Pembroke WV698 was first flown on 20 November 1952 and, in addition to RAF use, was exported to Belgium, Finland, Sudan, Sweden and Germany.

The Prince G-23-1/G-ALCM first flew at Luton on 13 May 1948 and was advertised as follows:

> Percival Prince – designed for Feeder Lines and Charter work, the Prince a new medium Transport Aircraft, is an all metal, high wing Monoplane with nosewheel undercarriage, seating 8-10 passengers. Powered by two 505 hp Alvis Leonides engines driving constant speed, feathering and braking propellers. Cruising at 170 mph at 6,000 ft using only 50% power, with a top speed of well over 200 mph. 8 passengers, 2 crew, 400 lb of baggage over a range of 800 miles. Designed for use with wheels, floats or skis.

Production of the Prince family comprised:

- Civil variants: Twenty-six P.50 Prince and P.54 Survey Prince, five P.66 President (civilian equivalent to Pembroke).
- Forty-eight P.57 Sea Prince in three variants.
- 128 P.66 Pembroke.

The Prince series was produced in some numbers by Hunting Percival at Luton. This is Sea Prince C.1 WF137. (J.S. Smith)

The Pembroke was developed from the Prince light transport for military communications duties. 128 were built for the RAF and five export customers. (Author)

More than 450 examples of the unglamorous but functional Provost trainer were built, the type also being the progenitor of the Jet Provost and Strikemaster. (Author)

The P.56 Provost prototype flew for the first time on 23 February 1950. The two prototypes, WE522 and WE530, were powered by the Armstrong Siddeley Cheetah, this engine being replaced in production aircraft by the Alvis Leonides. The Provost trainer was exported to Rhodesia, Ireland, Malaya, Burma, Iraq, Muscat and Oman, and Sudan, in addition to 391 aircraft for the RAF, total production being 461 aircraft.

The company name changed to **Hunting Percival Aircraft Ltd** on 26 April 1954, some ten years after Percival Aircraft Ltd had come under the control of the Hunting group. The P.84 Jet Provost prototype XD674 first flew on 26 June 1954. The Jet Provost T.3 flew on 22 June 1958. In 1957, the company was advertising: 'Jet Provost – The only turbo-jet aircraft in the world to have been accepted for the ab initio training of military pilots.' By 1962, the success of the type in the export market rendered the prose/praise more fulsome: 'RAF, Royal Ceylon AF, Sudan AF, Kuwait AF all choose the Jet Provost: Recent orders placed by Sudan and Kuwait emphasise the world-wide suitability of the Jet Provost – the world's most efficient trainer of modern pilots Provisioned with weapons the Jet Provost may be used for armament training and ground attack. It is the standard basic primary trainer in service with the Royal Air Force.' The type was further developed by BAC at Warton in the form of the Jet Provost T. Mk 5, and the BAC 167 Strikemaster. The production of the early marks of Jet Provost included 185 T.4 and 201 T.3; total production of all marks for the RAF and six export countries was 588 aircraft. These figures exclude production of the BAC Strikemaster.

The Helicopter Division of Hunting Percival briefly flirted with the helicopter in the guise of the fish-shaped P.74 XK889, which resolutely refused to fly in mid-1956.

The company name changed to **Hunting Aircraft Ltd** on 5 December 1957 and it became part of the **British Aircraft Corporation** in 1960, becoming fully incorporated as **British Aircraft Corporation (Luton) Ltd** from January 1964. The Hunting H.107 project became the basis of the successful BAC One-Eleven. The Luton operations of the

Above: *The Jet Provost served with distinction as a basic trainer for the RAF. This is a Jet Provost T.3A, which previously served with the RAF as XM405. (Author)*

Left: *A 1962 advertisment for the Jet Provost from the British Aircraft Corporation. (BAE SYSTEMS plc)*

ROYAL AIR FORCE
ROYAL CEYLON AIR FORCE
SUDAN AIR FORCE
KUWAIT AIR FORCE

ALL CHOOSE THE *Jet Provost*

BRISTOL SIDDELEY VIPER TURBOJET

Recent orders placed by Sudan and Kuwait emphasise the world wide suitability of the Jet Provost—the most efficient trainer of modern pilots. Provisioned for weapons the Jet Provost may be used for armament training and ground attack. It is the standard primary basic trainer in service with the Royal Air Force.

 BRITISH AIRCRAFT CORPORATION
ONE HUNDRED PALL MALL LONDON SW1 ENGLAND

TCA BHP13

British Aircraft Corporation ceased in December 1966, responsibility for the Jet Provost passing to the Preston Division of BAC. The closure of Luton was a consequence of company restructuring following the cancellation of the TSR.2.

Woburn Abbey

Although not a manufacturing site, it is interesting to note that Short Stirling aircraft were stored at Woburn Abbey during the Second World War and used the narrow sloping strip, which is more suitable for its current use by attendees at the annual de Havilland Moth Club Rally. Around the time of D-Day there were some 200 Stirlings on site, mainly for modification to allow their use for glider towing. Stirling aircraft were typically delivered to Marwell, Keevil and Fairford to replace those lost during the Arnhem operations.

Known as No.34 SLG, the site was used by No.6 MU (Abingdon) and handled a wide variety of aircraft, including Spitfire, Hurricane, Battle, Master, Tiger Moth, Magister, Swordfish, and Albacore. In February 1943, the site was transferred to No.8 MU (Little Rissington), who were responsible for the aforementioned Short Stirling operations. The site was closed in May 1947. (Source: Author's information augmented by material from Barry Abraham.)

Cambridgeshire

Bourn

The Short Brothers Repair Organisation was located at Bourn during the Second World War, for further details, see Cambridge.

Cambridge

The **AJD** Avro 504K replica G-ECKE was flown at Teversham on 29 September 1994 by the late Robin Bowes, see also Milden, Suffolk.

The **de Bruyne** Snark G-ADDL (later L6103) was built and developed at Cambridge, and was first flown by Dr Norman de Bruyne from Marshall's Fen Ditton airfield (north west of the present airport) on 16 December 1934. The Snark was long winged, in the style of the day, but most notably featured stressed-skin construction using thin skins of bakelite-bonded plywood. Much of the construction of the Snark was carried out by Mr S.F. Wilkinson, assistant to Dr de Bruyne, and author of *The Construction of Wooden Aircraft*.

Dr de Bruyne's second design, the Ladybird, which first flew from Marshall's Cambridge Airport on 6 January 1938, was the first type to make use of the new adhesives invented by de Bruyne. The Ladybird featured a stressed-skin fuselage and a tricycle undercarriage of very narrow track, with trousered main legs. The aircraft was powered initially by a Scott Squirrel, which was later replaced by a Bristol Cherub. The Ladybird was sold, prior to completion, to Mr J.N. Maas of Grantchester, and is sometimes referred to as the de Bruyne-Maas Ladybird. At the time of its first flight, the aircraft was prominently marked DB3-M1 (de Bruyne3-Maas1), being subsequently registered as G-AFEG. The Ladybird was constructed at Duxford, which see for additional information on the pioneering work of Dr de Bruyne.

Marshall (Cambridge) Limited was registered as a limited company in 1934, taking over the garage business founded as The Brunswick Motor Car Co. by D.G. Marshall in 1909. During the First World War the company name was changed to Marshall's Garage. The garage extended its interests into the aircraft industry with the opening of its first small aerodrome at Fen Ditton on 9 June 1929.

This airfield was set up initially by Arthur Marshall at Whitehill Farm, as a convenient field from which to fly his own Gipsy Moth. The airfield was known unofficially as Marshall's Aerodrome, and officially as Cambridge (Fen Ditton). Marshall subsequently operated a flying school here, before RAF flying training expansion led to the move of a few hundred yards to the new airfield built by Marshall's at Teversham. Marshall's Flying School Ltd was established and registered as a limited company in 1934, removing all aviation responsibility from the garage company. By 1936 Marshall's were training pilots at the rate of ninety-six new 'A' licence private pilots per year, plus thirty renewals.

The aircraft activities of the company sprang out of Arthur Marshall's Flying Training activities at Fen Ditton and at Teversham. The company was later renamed **Marshall of Cambridge (Engineering) Ltd**, and then **Marshall of Cambridge Aerospace Ltd.** Marshall remain based at Teversham Airport, which was officially opened by the Air Minister, Sir Kingsley Wood, on 8 October 1938, although it had been in use from 21 October 1937, on which date Fen Ditton closed. Wartime activity included a number of major aircraft modification contracts, an activity that continues today.

In addition to its aircraft repair and modification activities (described below), Marshall's made an important contribution to the training of both pilots and instructors for the RAF from 1938 onward. From February 1938, the company operated an Elementary and Advanced Training School at Cambridge for the RAF Volunteer Reserve. This was supplemented by a further Volunteer Reserve School at Kidlington (opened in June 1938), and an RAF direct entry Elementary Flying Training School at Cambridge from early 1939. This latter became the largest such centre in the country with 240 residential pupils and no less than 180 aircraft. A Supplementary Flying Instructor School was opened in May 1941, building upon Marshall's own innovative Ab Initio Flying Instructor Scheme. This saw

Marshall of Cambridge made an important contribution to wartime pilot and instructor training, the aircraft used being the Miles Master and de Havilland Tiger Moth. (Marshall Aerospace Ltd)

The Hawker Typhoon aircraft was one of many types to be repaired by Marshall of Cambridge during the Second World War. This photograph was taken in autumn 1944. (Marshall Aerospace Ltd)

students of high promise being taken direct from their initial flying instruction and streamed through directly as advanced flying training instructors, without having had four or five years squadron service (as had been the previous practice). In September 1941, there was a further expansion, with the opening of a further RAF Elementary Flight Training School at Clyffe Pypard, near Swindon, with 106 aircraft.

Early contracts fulfilled by Marshall of Cambridge comprised the modification and repair of all RAF Whitley aircraft, an activity that continued throughout the Second World War. To support this effort, the company had a complete set of manufacturing jigs for rebuilding, repairs, modification and development. The Aircraft Repair Organisation set up by Marshall's subsequently handled repair and modification of the Gladiator, Hart, Hind, Oxford, Albemarle, B-17 Flying Fortress, Mosquito, Typhoon, Dakota and Hamilcar X at Cambridge, in addition to Spitfire, Hurricane and Hampden repairs carried out off-site. Over 5,000 aircraft were repaired or modified for other duties by this organisation at Cambridge, and at over thirty RAF sites from Devon to Lossiemouth.

Ninety-eight Mosquito were converted to NF. Mk XII in 1943, to be followed by 100 to be converted to NF. Mk XVII. Marshall's also carried out a number of conversions to enable the Mosquito B.IV to carry a single 4,000lb bomb. Other work included B.IV deck landing modifications and conversion of a limited number of aircraft for use in 'Highball' experiments (carried out jointly with other contractors).

In 1953, Marshall of Cambridge were contracted to build the last eighty-four de Havilland DH112 Venom, constructing fifty Venom FB.1 (the first being WE414) and thirty-four Venom FB.4. This was a most welcome contract for the company who had become much involved in commercial vehicle coach building to maintain employment and efficient use of

Assembly of new-build de Havilland Venom fighters. Marshall's built fifty FB.1 and thirty-four FB.4. (Marshall Aerospace Ltd)

In 1975, Marshall's prepared eleven B(I)68 Canberra aircraft for export to the Peruvian Air Force. The company also conducted repair, modification and upgrade work on RAF Canberra aircraft. (Marshall Aerospace Ltd)

Only ten Belfast were built to fulfil the RAF heavy-lift role. This example is under test from Cambridge following conversion to civil use by Marshall of Cambridge. (Author)

existing production capacity. Marshall's were also involved in the repair and rebuild of Vampire aircraft, this work being undertaken at Waterbeach, where the necessary hard runway was available. The initial repair and rebuild activities were followed by new-build Vampire aircraft for export (for example, to Iraq).

Venom production at Cambridge resulted in the construction of a large runway, which has served the company well ever since, allowing them to handle work on large aircraft of all types. From 1954 onward, the company converted 284 Vampire T.11 aircraft to ejector-seat configuration, including the fitting of modified cockpit canopies.

Conversions to produce an electronic reconnaissance variant of the Comet, the Comet R.2, were carried out by the RAF and Marshall of Cambridge. A total of seven aircraft were converted based on three civil Comet 2 and four military Comet C.2.

Extensive overhaul and modification work has been performed on such types as Vickers Viking, Valetta and Varsity (modifications to sixty-one aircraft); Bristol Brigand (twenty-three fitted with radar noses); Vickers Valiant; Airspeed Ambassador; Grumman Gulfstream; English Electric Canberra (in-service repairs, modifications and developments, conversions from B.6 to B.15 and B.16, and preparation for export); Vickers Viscount and Vanguard; Bristol Britannia (including cockpit modifications for BOAC); Comet; BAC One-Eleven; and BAC VC10. In January 1961, the company was advertising for fitters and inspectors for work on the Vanguard, Viscount, Valiant and Comet. Surplus RAF Short Belfast aircraft were converted by Marshall's and certified for civil use.

The Marshall MA4 boundary layer control research aircraft, VF665, based on the prototype Auster T.7, flew in early 1959 (some sources state autumn 1961). The MA4 featured a porous wing surface, boundary layer suction being used to increase lift and delay flow separation.

Enlarged tail surfaces were required to maintain directional and longitudinal stability at the low speeds that the aircraft could achieve (with their associated high downwash velocities). When fully developed, the aircraft demonstrated stalling speeds as low as 30 knots (to the delight of the test team, slower than their Tiger Moth photographic chase aircraft). Regrettably, the aircraft was destroyed in a fatal accident in March 1966 after some 120 hours of experimental flying.

In 1961 Marshall's converted a single Beagle Airedale to a Continental GO-300E engine, allowing it to be displayed at the Farnborough SBAC show of that year with a (nominally) British engine, Rolls-Royce Ltd having taken a Continental manufacturing licence. The company also designed and manufactured the droop nose and retracting cockpit visor for the Concorde aircraft.

Marshall of Cambridge became the UK sister design authority to Lockheed on the C-130 Hercules and was responsible for the UK stretched Hercules programme, modifying twenty-nine aircraft at Cambridge. Hercules work has also been carried out for a large number of other users from many countries; by 1999 work had been carried out for forty-two civil and military operators from thirty-four nations.

The company was responsible for the conversion of the RAF Meteorological Research W. Mk 2 Hercules XV208 (first flown on 21 March 1973); two Buccaneer aircraft used in support of the Tornado development programme; and modification of Vulcan XA903 as a test bed for the RB199 (first flown on 12 April 1973). The company carried out six conversions of TriStar aircraft to tanker configuration, the first aircraft ZD950 flying on 9 July 1985. Modifications to allow the air to air refuelling of RAF C-130 aircraft were developed and implemented within three weeks in 1982, during the Falklands conflict. Further modifications to allow the C-130 to operate as a tanker aircraft were completed within six weeks.

Today Marshall Aerospace performs depot maintenance of the RAF E-3D Sentry and continues its TriStar freight conversion programme, and Gulfstream and Hercules support. The company also prepares all C-130J Hercules aircraft prior to their delivery for RAF service.

XT272 was one of the two Buccaneer aircraft modified for trials in support of the development of the Tornado. (Marshall Aerospace Ltd)

The **Short Brothers Repair Organisation (SEBRO)** had facilities at Madingley Rd, Cambridge, and at RAF Bourn. SEBRO employed a peak workforce of 4,500 to carry out the repair of accident and battle damaged Stirling bombers. The factory site was purpose built, and by 1941, no less than seven large production hangars were in use, with further extensions on the site in 1942. Incoming aircraft for repair were either flown in to Bourn, or (more normally) delivered by road to Bourn. Their repair needs were then assessed – irreparable cases were cannibalised for their instruments and other reusable components. After repair, the aircraft were moved back to RAF Bourn from Maddingley by road, re-assembled, and flight-tested. Later in the war, SEBRO carried out conversions of the Stirling for use in other roles. SEBRO closed in 1946.

Wg Cdr Ken **Wallis** set up a company at 121 Chesterton Road, Cambridge to test the market for autogyros. One was sold to Norfolk & Norwich Flying Club at Swanton Morley and flown there from 1964 to 1967.

Duxford

The **de Bruyne** Ladybird was built by **Aero Research Ltd** of Hinxton Road, Duxford – Dr Norman de Bruyne's company, which was engaged in the development of new forms of synthetic adhesive, notably the synthetic glue Aerolite for use in wooden structures, and the Redux metal to metal bonding process. Other fields of research included fabric impregnated with artificial resin, and the jointing of plastic materials. From a public perspective, the company's most famous product is probably the adhesive Araldite. Construction of the Ladybird was the responsibility of Mr George Newell who was later responsible for the development of the Redux metal-to-metal adhesive.

Dr de Bruyne, who died in 1997, also used his bonding process to create aluminium honeycomb structures, and this development, together with the adhesives themselves, had an immense influence on subsequent aircraft structural design.

The company origin was the **Cambridge Aircraft Construction Co. Ltd**, which was formed in 1931, changing its name to **Aero Research Ltd** in April 1934. Control of Aero Research Ltd passed to Ciba-Geigy in May 1948, Dr de Bruyne remaining as managing director until 1960 (see also Cambridge for details of the Ladybird and the earlier de Bruyne Snark).

Duxford airfield is the home of many restoration and maintenance organisations looking after historic and, in particular, Second World War aircraft. These include **Historic Flying Ltd**, which was originally based at Audley End, Essex, moving to Duxford in April 2001. The company specialises in the restoration to flying condition of Spitfire aircraft. Restorations to date are summarised below, noting that only the more recently flown aircraft have been completed at Duxford.

Type	Serial	Comments
Spitfire LF. Mk XVIe	RW382	G-XVIA, first flight after rebuild 3 July 1991. Previously gate guardian at RAF Leconfield.
Spitfire Mk IX	TE566	G-BLCK, first flown after rebuild on 2 July 1992. Recovered from a kibbutz in Israel.
Spitfire FR. Mk XVIIIe	TP280	G-BTXE, first flown after rebuild on 5 July 1992. Aircraft recovered from India.
Spitfire LF. Mk XVIe	TD248	G-OXVI, previously the gate guardian at RAF Sealand, flown on 10 November 1992.
Mosquito	RR299	In 1992, Historic Flying obtained the contract to renew the fabric on British Aerospace's historic but ill-fated Mosquito RR299.

Type	Serial	Comments
Spitfire Mk XIV	NH799	G-BUZU, first flown after rebuild on 21 January 1994. Aircraft recovered from India.
Spitfire Mk XIV	SM832	G-WWII, first flown after rebuild on 22 May 1995. Aircraft recovered from India.
Spitfire LF. Mk Vb	EP120	G-LFVB, first flown after rebuild on 12 September 1995.
Spitfire PR.XIX	PM631	Winter overhaul 1995/96 for the Battle of Britain Memorial Flight.
Hurricane	LF363	Rebuilt for the Battle of Britain Memorial Flight following accident. Flown on 29 September 1998.
Spitfire Mk Vb	BM597	G-MKVB, ex-RAF gate guardian at Hednesford, Bridgnorth, Church Fenton. First flown after restoration 17 July 1997.
Spitfire Mk Vc	AR614	G-BUWA, returned to the UK from Canada. Flown at Audley End on 5 October 1996.
Spitfire FR. XVIIIe	SM845	G-BUOS, ex-Indian Air Force HHS687. First flown after restoration 7 July 2000.
Spitfire Vb	AB910	Refurbished in late 1996/early 1997 for the RAF Battle of Britain Memorial Flight.
Seafire LF. IIIc	PP972	Survey only.
Spitfire LF. Mk IXc	MK912	Flown after restoration on 8 September 2000, G-BRRA.
Spitfire Mk Vc	JG891	Awaiting restoration 2002.
Spitfire Mk XIV	RN201	G-BSKP, first flight after restoration 24 April 2002, Duxford.
Spitfire Tr.IX	IAAC 161/ PV202	G-TRIX under rebuild after major accident damage at Goodwood 15 September 1996.
Spitfire IX	'UB424'	Ex-Burmese aircraft awaiting restoration 2002.

The work of Spitfire restoration continues with four to six aircraft likely to be under restoration at any one time.

Fulbourn (near Cambridge)

Wallbro Monoplane: The 'Wallbro' (**Wall**is **bro**thers) Monoplane was 'hopped' in 1910 at Fulbourn, near Cambridge, before being damaged beyond repair in a storm that destroyed its hangar in October 1910. The brothers Horace and Percival Wallis founded a company to promote the type, this being the **Wallis Aeroplane Co.**, of 12 St Barnabas Road, Cambridge. This address was the Wallis family home, at which the monoplane was constructed between 1908 and 1910. The machine was completed in May 1910, being placed on public view on 16-17 May. The advertising material ahead of this event indicated that Messrs Wallis Bros 'having had numerous requests from friends and the public to see their new monoplane, they have decided to place it on view to the public [...] from 11 to 7.30 each day at 12 St Barnabas' Road, Cambridge. The machine will be staked down and the motor and tractor SET RUNNING at 12 and 4 o'clock each day.' The machine was also described in an article published in the *Cambridge Daily News* of 12 May 1910. This praised the 'extremely graceful and workmanlike lines on which it is built', and 'the sound and truly British work that has been put into it'.

The aircraft was then moved, with help from a Spratt's horse-drawn wagon, to a field near Fleam Dyke at Fulbourn. The aircraft was flown or hopped on several occasions, sustaining damage when it was turned over on 4 July 1910. In *British Aircraft before the Great War* the comment is made that 'there is no record of sustained flight'. The machine is chiefly notable for its use of steel tube construction, a material with which the brothers were familiar from their experience of building and racing motorcycles. Power was provided by a 25hp V-4 JAP engine, and the type was fitted with ailerons, rather than using wing warping.

*The Wallis Brothers photographed with their 1910 **Wallbro** Monoplane, which was distinguished by its steel tube construction. (Ian J.E. Hancock)*

Horace and Percival were, respectively, the father and uncle of Wg Cdr Ken Wallis MBE of Reymerston Hall, Suffolk, who is well known for his autogyro research and development. Wg Cdr Wallis constructed a replica of the Wallbro Monoplane using modern materials and powered by a 72hp McCulloch engine. The Wallis Wallbro replica G–BFIP was first flown on 10 August 1978 from RAF Swanton Morley, Norfolk.

Horsey Toll

Horsey Toll, to the east of Peterborough, was used by **The Aeronautical Corporation of Great Britain** for the test-flying of their Peterborough-built Aeronca aircraft. After the demise of that enterprise, its successor **Peterborough Aircraft Co. Ltd** continued to use Horsey Toll for development of the Ely, an improved version of the Aeronca. Peterborough Flying Club Ltd (having the same directors as the aircraft company) operated from Horsey Toll. At the beginning of the Second World War, the company was engaged in the development of a high-wing light aircraft, the Peterborough Guardian. The Guardian was allocated the registration G–AFZT, but was never flown.

Morrisons: During the Second World War, the airfield housed a unit of the Civilian Repair Organisation dealing with Hurricanes, which was managed by Morrisons 'of Croydon and Peterborough'. **Morrisons Engineering Ltd** were advertising in 1945 using an artist's impression of a Hawker Hurricane, and the slogan 'Morrisons Croydon and elsewhere. Construction, Maintenance and Repair'. By 1946, the text was more specific as to location: 'Morrisons – Croydon and Peterborough, Aircraft Construction, Maintenance and Repair. To the private owner we offer the same aircraft maintenance and repair service that we rendered

A 1946 advertisement for
Morrisons.

to the fighting services.' In 1947, the company was advertising itself under the slogan 'Construction, Maintenance and Repair', and listing two subsidiary firms – Morrisons Engineering Ltd and Morrisons Aircraft Services with offices at 11 Upper Grosvenor Street, London W1.

Huntingdon

The racing driver and pioneer pilot **James Radley** began flying in 1910, subsequently touring various flying meetings and exhibitions in Britain and in the USA with his Blériot, before engaging in the design of his own machines. Radley's Blériot was consistently faster than similar machines flown by other pilots. Radley subsequently produced the **Radley-Moorhouse** Monoplane 1911, and **Radley-England** Waterplane.

The **Radley-Moorhouse** Monoplane was a Blériot development with a fully covered fuselage. It was reported in October 1911 that the machine was flying well and that tests were continuing. The monoplane proved a successful racer, and was still being flown actively at Hendon in summer 1914.

James Radley founded **Portholme Aerodrome Ltd** of St John's Street, Huntingdon. The eponymous aerodrome at Portholme Meadow (also described as the disused Port Holme racecourse) is reputed to have been the largest meadow in England. Within its 309 acres, a three-mile circuit was possible. The field was, however, extremely flat with the unfortunate result that the whole field became flooded when the nearby River Ouse rose. The company name was changed in the spring of 1911 to **Portholme Aerodrome Co.**, marking the joining of the company by W.B. Rhodes Moorhouse. In September 1911, the company was advertising 'Hangars to let on the best aerodrome in England'. In June 1912, the Huntingdon aeroplane stock of Messrs Radley and Moorhouse was sold to Handley Page.

Portholme Aerodrome Co. Ltd: 'Best aerodrome in England'.

Handley Page Ltd: the acquisition of the stock of Radley and Moorhouse.

In 1913 E.C. Gordon England joined James Radley at Huntingdon. The Radley-England Waterplane was initially tested at Huntingdon in 1913 as a landplane, before testing moved to Shoreham. The Radley-England Waterplane was the world's first three-engined machine, the three 50hp Gnome engines driving a single propeller. Another novel feature was that accommodation for the pilot and up to six passengers was provided in the floats.

After building armoured cars for the RNAS, aircraft contracts followed, initially with the Wight Type 840, eight of which were delivered as spares, followed by Sopwith designs. The company built the Camel (250, the first being B4601) and the Snipe (144 aircraft). The production details for the Snipe were rather complex: Portholme Aerodrome built only thirty-three of their first Snipe order (for 500 aircraft), the remainder of this order being completed by Ruston, Proctor & Co. Ltd. Portholme then built a batch of 100 Snipe, followed by just eleven from a final order for 300, some eighty-nine of which were completed by Ruston, Proctor & Co. Ltd.

In January 1918, the business name was again changed to **Portholme Aircraft Co. Ltd.** The company was wound up in March 1918, and a receiver appointed in June 1922.

In autumn 1998, *Popular Flying* reported the first flight of **Campbell Cricket** Mk IV autogyro prototype G-BXEM from a strip near Huntingdon. This aircraft was built by Peter Lovegrove of Didcot. Another example of this variant is registered G-BVLD. The origins of the Campbell Cricket design are presented under Hungerford and Membury, Berkshire, in *British Built Aircraft: Volume 3*.

Peterborough

This entry describes the activities of Frederick Sage & Co. during the First World War, followed by the manufacture of Aeronca aircraft in the same premises at Walton, Peterborough in the 1930s.

An advert for Sage & Co. Ltd extolling the qualities of their contract-built Short 184 aircraft for the RNAS.

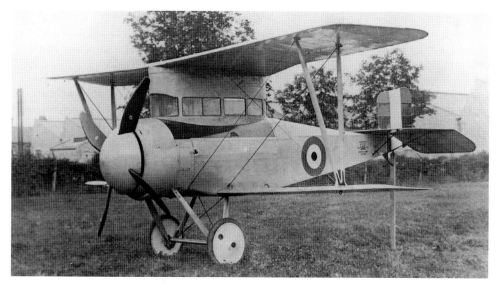

The Sage Type Scout featured a cockpit enclosure for the pilot and gunner. the gunner standing to command an all-round field of fire above the top wing. (Ken Ellis collection)

N5280 is the first of two Sage Type 3 training machines to be built. (Bristol AiRchive)

Frederick Sage & Co. Ltd was a firm of shopfitting woodworkers who constructed aircraft under contract, and designed their own types. The company advertised itself as 'Designers and manufacturers of Aeroplanes, Airships and all classes of aircraft. Contractors to the Admiralty'. Sage obtained their first aircraft order in the first week of July 1915 (*Flight*). The company installed Curtiss engines in BE2C, and built a large number of Avro 504K (at least 408 of 450 ordered) and seventy-two Short 184, in addition to their own Sage Type 2 Scout, and the Sage Type 3 and 4. The company also built Avro-designed airship gondolas.

E.C. Gordon England (late of **The British & Colonial Aeroplane Co. Ltd, James Radley**, and **J. Samuel White**) was the General Manager of Sage & Co., joining them in

September 1915, at which time the company was expanding fast, doubling its capacity and acquiring additional premises. A large workshop was built which measured 250ft long, 55ft wide, and 25ft to its rafters. By November 1917, the company was adopting a rather flowery style of advertising – 'The Empire of the Air is to be won by the infinite capacity for taking pains. The lead which Sage Aircraft has taken is the result of intense application to the perfection of design and workmanship. E.C. Gordon England, AFRAeS, Aviation Department.'

The Sage Type 2 first flew on 10 August 1916, and was distinguished by an enclosed cockpit, and a gunner station fitted above the top wing. Such a cumbersome arrangement was considered necessary, due to the lack of a reliable interrupter mechanism. The aircraft was destroyed in an accident on 20 September 1916. The Sage Type 3 was a simple and attractive primary trainer, which first flew in early 1917, and was followed by the similar Sage Type 4, which flew on 3 July 1917. An order for 130 Sopwith Ship's Camel, placed with Sage, was cancelled.

During the Second World War, Frederick Sage & Co. Ltd were responsible, among many other dispersed contractors, for the manufacture of Horsa components, including 415 front fuselage sections.

Aeronca – the **Aeronautical Corporation of Great Britain Ltd** – was set up in 1936 to build a British version of the American Aeronca C-3. British-built aircraft were constructed at Peterborough, in the ex-Sage factory at Walton and taken to nearby Horsey Toll for flight testing. The Peterborough-built Aeronca was fitted with the JAP-99 engine, and was known as the Aeronca 100. According to A.J. Jackson's *British Civil Aircraft since 1919*, production totalled twenty-one Aeronca 100 (of which details have not been traced of one aircraft), a single Ely (Aeronca 300), and two Ely 700 (see below).

The flying clubs at Peterborough and at Hanworth used a number of Aeroncas. Flg Off. Llewellyn flew the American-built C-3 G-AEAC to Johannesburg in twenty-three days in early 1936. The Aeronautical Corporation of Great Britain encountered trading difficulties, having failed to find buyers for a number of aircraft that had already been completed, and entered liquidation on 5 November 1937.

G-AEVS is an Aeronca 100, built in Peterborough by the Aeronautical Corporation of Great Britain Ltd. (Author)

The Aeronca activity also spawned the **Peterborough Aircraft Co. Ltd**, this company being registered with £100 capital on 16 September 1938, with offices in Park Lane. This firm produced an Aeronca 100 development under the designation Peterborough Ely. This type was characterised by a number of design improvements, including an increase in fuselage length and width. G-AEVE carried the name Ely on the rudder and was also widely known as the Aeronca 300.

A later version was known as the Ely 700, two aircraft being registered as G-AFLU and G-AFLT. The design differences that distinguished this variant have not been recorded. G-AFXC was allocated to a further development known as the Ely Type F.C.1, but this was not completed.

The **Brown** Monoplane was a low-wing monoplane that is reported to have been constructed in the 1930s using Aeronca 100 components. The Brown Monoplane was flown unregistered. Note that this information may not be wholly reliable, in that the machine is not mentioned in Ord-Hume's *British Light Aeroplanes – Their Evolution, Development and Perfection 1920-40*, this author's coverage of such irregular types being particularly comprehensive.

The Sage/Aeronca factory still exists at Walton, just off the A1 to the north of Peterborough. The factory buildings are characteristic of their period, and further evidence of their origins is provided by their being sited just off *Sage* Lane.

RAF Waterbeach (near Cambridge)

RAF Waterbeach was used by **Marshall of Cambridge (Engineering) Ltd** for their Vampire and Venom activities, taking advantage of the availability of a hard runway at Waterbeach. Initial activities were mainly Vampire repair and rebuild work, followed by new-build Vampire aircraft for export (for example, to Iraq). Other work included modification of three pre-production Swift in 1952.

RAF Wittering

Handley Page Ltd: The Handley Page Hastings prototype TE580 first flew at RAF Wittering on 3 May 1946. Two prototypes were followed by 144 Hastings for the RAF, the type remaining in service from 1948 until 1968. Four additional Hastings C.3 served with the RNZAF, giving a production total of 150. The type's general characteristics are summed up in Handley Page advertising of 1947:

> *Hastings, Britain's largest and fastest transport is for the Royal Air Force. Its multipurpose roles include freighter paratrooper, ambulance, troop transport and glider tug. Seven and a half tons of military equipment – guns, lorries, etc – can be carried. Hastings has a top speed of 354 mph and range of 3,260 miles.*

Derbyshire

Church Broughton

This airfield, to the west of Derby and previously an RAF OTU, was used by **Rolls-Royce Ltd** for jet engine flight testing. The Trent Meteor EE227, the world's first turboprop aircraft, was first flown at Church Broughton on 20 September 1945. Details of Rolls-Royce test bed aircraft are given under Hucknall.

Derby

The **LMS Railway** works at Derby carried out work on Hurricane wings during the Second World War. The organisation was initially the Hampden Bomber Repair Organisation, and subsequently worked on Lancaster repairs in conjunction with A.V. Roe & Co. Ltd at Langar and Bracebridge Heath, and Tollerton Aircraft Services at Tollerton Airfield, Nottingham. Some of the Hampden and Lancaster work was sub-contracted to Brush Coachworks Ltd at Loughborough.

Herefordshire & Worcestershire

Kidderminster

Short Brothers (Rochester & Bedford) Ltd: Owing to the effects of bombing at Rochester in August 1940, and the threat of further raids, the decision was taken to disperse production of the Stirling. One consequence was the removal to Kidderminster of the Shorts design and drawing office, where it remained from late 1940 until the end of 1942.

Leicestershire

Bitteswell Airfield (west of Lutterworth)

Bitteswell was used by **Sir W.G. Armstrong Whitworth Aircraft Ltd**, and its successors, as both a factory, and as a flight test airfield. Other sites used include Baginton (Coventry Airport, Warwickshire); Parkside, Coventry; and Whitley Abbey, which see for further information.

Sir W.G. Armstrong Whitworth Aircraft Ltd first used Bitteswell for Avro Lancaster assembly and flight test from 1943. The major types manufactured by Sir W.G. Armstrong Whitworth Aircraft Ltd, and flown from Bitteswell are listed below:

Type	Numbers produced and comments
Avro Lancaster	A total of 1,329 comprising 919 Mk I, 300 Mk II, 110 Mk III. Some of the Armstrong Whitworth-built Lancaster II aircraft were assembled at Sywell, Northampton. Other dispersed facilities were operated at Leicester and Nuneaton. Some aircraft assembled and flown at Bitteswell.
Gloster Meteor (later marks)	Forty-five Meteor F.4; 430 Meteor F.8 (the last aircraft being converted to prone pilot configuration); and 615 night fighter Meteor made up as follows: 352 NF.11 for the RAF (plus three prototypes and twenty aircraft exported to Denmark), 100 NF.12 (prototype WS590, flown 21 April 1953), forty NF.13 (prototype WM308, flown 21 December 1952), and 100 NF.14 (prototype WM261 (from NF.12)).
Hawker Sea Hawk	520 Sea Hawk assembled at Bitteswell (all except the first thirty-five aircraft, which were assembled by Hawker Aircraft Ltd at Kingston and test-flown at Dunsfold).
Gloster Javelin	133 (marks FAW. 6, 7, 9 at Bitteswell) see additional comments below.
Hawker Hunter	278 Hunter (marks as follows: forty-five F.2; 105 F.5; 128 F.6); and four Hunter T.7 and at least fourteen T.8 conversions from F.4.
Armstrong Whitworth Argosy	Eighteen civil (A.W.650) and fifty-six military Argosy (A.W.660). The civil machines ended their active lives with Sagittair/Air Bridge Carriers at Castle Donington, and Midland Air Cargo at Coventry.

Although the majority of the 1,329 Armstrong Whitworth-built Lancaster aircraft were assembled at Baginton, a number of aircraft were assembled and flown from Bitteswell. From 1953 onward, all Baginton-built aircraft were assembled and flight-tested at Bitteswell. Prior to 1954, there is some uncertainty as to which aircraft were flown at Baginton and which at Bitteswell, and many first flights were used to reposition the aircraft from Baginton to Bitteswell for further testing As indicated in the table above, the most important Armstrong Whitworth aircraft to be test-flown at Bitteswell included the Meteor, Javelin, Hunter, and Sea Hawk, for which the (then) grass airfield at Baginton was unsuitable. The freehold of Bitteswell airfield was purchased by Armstrong Whitworth in 1956.

The A.W.52G flying wing glider (RG324) was tested at Bitteswell (some sources indicate Baginton) on 2 March 1945 towed by a Whitley, subsequently flying at Beaulieu and Boscombe Down. The much larger jet-powered A.W.52 TS363 was first flown at Boscombe Down on 13 November 1947, and then tested at Bitteswell and Baginton. In March 1947, advertising copy was emphasising that AWA were at the forefront of modern developments: 'Armstrong Whitworth Aircraft – Pacemakers of Progress. Designers and constructors of modern Tailless Aircraft and Swept-back Wings.'

Meteor EE445 was modified for experimental testing of the Griffith boundary layer control wing section, this aircraft flying at Bitteswell on 21 January 1947. Many of the later Meteor aircraft (from the last batch of Meteor F. Mk 8 onward) were assembled and test-flown at Bitteswell. The Meteor NF.11 night fighter was developed with the assistance of a Meteor T.7

The Armstrong Whitworth A.W.52 TS363 seen at Bitteswell in December 1947, one month after its first flight at Boscombe Down. (BAE SYSTEMS plc via Ken Ellis)

This Armstrong Whitworth advertisement from March 1947 emphasises the company's forward-looking outlook.
(BAE SYSTEMS plc)

Armstrong Whitworth was responsible for Sea Hawk production.
(BAE SYSTEMS plc)

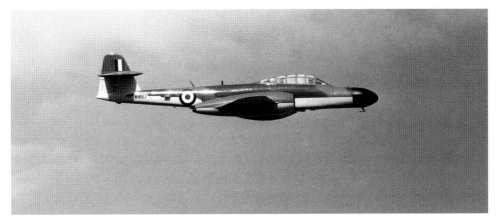

WM167 is a Gloster Meteor NF11/TT20. Like all night fighter versions of the Meteor, it was built in Coventry by Sir W.G. Armstrong Whitworth Aircraft Ltd. (Author)

A splendid line-up of a dozen brand new Sea Hawk at Bitteswell, photographed on 31 March 1954. (Ray Williams archive)

VW413 modified to represent the NF.11, which first flew at Bitteswell on 28 January 1949. In addition to new-build NF.11 production aircraft, twenty-six NF.11 aircraft (six of them Danish) were converted to target tug variants as the TT.20. Bitteswell also handled a number of Meteor aircraft for in-service modification work.

Sir W.G. Armstrong Whitworth Aircraft Ltd manufactured all but the first thirty-five Sea Hawk aircraft, some 520 being built, mainly at Bitteswell. The first Armstrong Whitworth-built Sea Hawk, WF162, flew on 16 January 1953. The Armstrong Whitworth production comprised: sixty F.1; forty F.2; 116 FB.3; ninety-seven FGA.4; eighty-seven FGA.6; twenty-two F.50 (Netherlands); thirty F.50 (India); thirty-four Mk 100 (Germany); and thirty-four Mk 101 (Germany).

Armstrong Whitworth manufactured 278 Hunter aircraft, and were responsible for the refurbishment of eighty-two of the type for export. A number of single-seat aircraft were converted to T.8 for use by the Royal Navy. (Author)

Armstrong Whitworth received extensive orders for the Hunter, supplementing production by Hawker Aircraft Ltd at Kingston/Dunsfold and at Blackpool. The first Bitteswell-built Hunter was F.2 WN888, which first flew on 14 October 1953. In addition to a new-build programme extending to 278 aircraft, Bitteswell participated in a long-running refurbishment programme, producing aircraft for the export market, in effect extending the already impressive production run of the type. The company also converted eighteen single-seat aircraft to T.8 configuration for the Royal Navy. The Hunter refurbishment programme was carried out under the aegis of Hawker Siddeley Aviation Ltd, see below.

Sir W.G. Armstrong Whitworth Aircraft Ltd manufactured 133 Gloster Javelin two-seat all-weather fighters, comprising thirty-two FAW.4, forty-four FAW.5 and fifty-seven FAW.7, some of which were modified on the production line to FAW.9 standard. The first Armstrong Whitworth-built aircraft, XA720, was flown on 23 February 1956.

The A.W.650 Argosy was a four-engine freight transport with a 'pod and twin-tailboom' configuration, The prototype G-AOZZ first flew from a snowy Bitteswell on 8 January 1959, with its military derivative the A.W.660 Argosy C.1 XN814 flying on 4 March 1961. The prototype of the improved civil Argosy Srs 200 G-ASKZ was first flown on 11 March 1964. A total of seventeen civil and fifty-six military variants were built.

The **Armstrong Siddeley Motors** flight test fleet was based at Bitteswell, although engine test work prior to the Second World War had also been conducted at Baginton. A summary of turbine engine test bed aircraft operated in support of Armstrong Siddeley engine development is given on page 100.

Above: *The Argosy prototype making its first flight at a snowy Bitteswell in January 1959.* (BAE SYSTEMS plc via Ken Ellis)

Right: *Armstrong Whitworth's final design to enter production was the Argosy. Fifty-size A.W.660 Argosy C.1 were built for the Royal Air Force.* (BAE SYSTEMS plc)

ARGOSY C. Mk. 1

◎ Choice of Transport Command

HAWKER SIDDELEY AVIATION

32 Duke Street, St. James's, London. S.W.1

Meteor WA820 set time to height records when fitted with Armstrong Siddeley Sapphire 2 engines. (BAE SYSTEMS plc)

Engine Type	Test Bed Fleet
Metropolitan-Vickers F.2 and F.2/4 Beryl	Lancaster BT308, flown with Metropolitan-Vickers F.2 in rear fuselage on 29 June 1943 (from Baginton). Lancaster B.2, LL735 flown with Metropolitan-Vickers F.2 in rear fuselage in 1944. Meteor RA490.
ASX	Lancaster ND784/G, first flown in June 1945, this aircraft later being flown with a nose mounted Mamba.
Python (turboprop ASX)	Lancaster TW911, two Python outboard, first flown 3 January 1949. Lancaster RE137, two Python outboard. Avro Lincoln RF403 (modified by AST at Hamble).
Mamba	Lancaster ND784/G, first flown 14 October 1947 at Hamble. Lancaster SW342 modification by AST, Hamble, January 1949. Dakota KJ839, flown 3 September 1949. Marathon VX231/G-AHXU, flown 21 July 1949.
Adder (jet version of Mamba)	Lancaster SW342 (simultaneously with Mamba in the nose). Flown in 1952.
Viper	Lancaster SW342, first flown November 1952. Also flown wing tip-mounted (and later with afterburner) on a Canberra. Viper 8 – test-flown in Hunting Percival Jet Provost G-42-1/G-AOBU.
Sapphire	A number of Hunter F.2 and F.5 were used by Armstrong Siddeley Motors for Sapphire development work, together with the following individual test bed aircraft:
Sapphire 1	Lancastrian VM733, first flown 19 January 1950 from Hamble following conversion by AST.

Engine Type	Test Bed Fleet
Sapphire 2	Meteor 8 WA820, first flown 14 August 1950. WA820 gained time to height records in this configuration, including 3 minutes 7 seconds to 39,370ft.
	Hastings TE583, Sapphires mounted in outboard nacelles, first flown 13 November 1950.
Sapphire 6	Canberra WD933, originally the prototype Canberra B.2.
Sapphire 7	Canberra WD933, first flown August 1954, also WK141, WK163 (in 1955), WV787 (Sapphire afterburner development in 1954).
	Avro Ashton WB491, WB494 icing trials.

The Hawker P.1040, VP401, was converted to 'mixed power' with an Armstrong Siddeley Snarler rocket motor to become the P.1072. The P.1072 was flown to Bitteswell on 16 November 1950, flying under mixed power for the first time on 20 November. The 3rd Balliol VL935 (Mamba powered) was test-flown from Bitteswell on 17 May 1948.

The Hawker P.1040 was converted to 'mixed-power' with the installation of an Armstrong Siddeley Snarler rocket motor to become the Hawker P.1072. (BAE SYSTEMS plc)

VL935, the third prototype of the Balliol, was powered by the Armstrong Siddeley Mamba, and made its first flight from Bitteswell in 1948. (Boulton Paul Asociation)

Hawker Siddeley Aviation Ltd (HSAL) took over from Sir W.G. Armstrong Whitworth Aircraft Ltd from 1963. After the completion of Argosy production, and the closure of the Baginton factory in 1965, Hawker Siddeley used Bitteswell for general repair and overhaul work. This was supplemented by a significant programme of Hawker Hunter refurbishment for export, which comprised eighty-two aircraft and ran from 1966 until 1973. Countries served by this programme included Chile, India, Iraq, Jordan, Lebanon, Qatar, Singapore and Switzerland.

The range of aircraft handled by the general overhaul programme was diverse, covering many of the other products of HSAL, including Javelin, Vulcan (113 individual aircraft), Trident 1 (thirteen aircraft repainted), Beverley, Gnat (seventy-two examples), HS.748, Nimrod, Shackleton (fifty examples), and Buccaneer (thirty-two aircraft). Conversion work on the Shackleton, to produce the AEW.2 version, was performed at Bitteswell (and Woodford). In another shared programme, Bitteswell carried out cockpit modifications for the Handley Page Victor K.2 conversion in support of the main programme at Woodford.

British Aerospace continued to use Bitteswell for repair and overhaul until the decision was taken to close the airfield in March 1982. Aircraft handled included the Hawk (at least twenty-three examples) and Harrier, in addition to some of the types listed above. From 1979 onward, thirty-nine new-build Hawk T.1 aircraft were built and test-flown at Bitteswell, providing additional capacity to the Kingston and Dunsfold sites, which were busy with Harrier work. The first Bitteswell-built Hawk XX291 flew on 29 November 1979, and the last, XX353, on 21 January 1982.

A number of blue painted hangars are still visible on the airfield, but the site is dominated by development associated with 'Europe's largest distribution centre'.

Bruntingthorpe (south of Leicester)

Gloster Meteor EE215 was used at Bruntingthorpe from February 1945 for testing reheat (afterburning) applied to its **Power Jets (Research & Development) Ltd** W.2/700 engines.

Castle Donington (East Midlands Airport)

Nipper Aircraft Ltd produced the Nipper Mk III at Castle Donington both as a factory-built aircraft, and in kit form. The company went into receivership in May 1971, rights being taken over by **Nipper Kits and Components Ltd** of Bromley, Kent, which was formed on 20 October 1971. This company supported the home-built movement, but did not build complete aircraft to order. Many of the Nipper Mk III airframes were manufactured under contract by Slingsby Aviation Ltd as the Slingsby T.56.

Coalville (near Loughborough)

Cascelloid Ltd, a doll manufacturer, assembled and tested Spitfire undercarriages as part of a Leicester-based dispersed manufacturing scheme. A grand total of 28,567 pairs of Spitfire main undercarriage legs were manufactured by this production group. (See also Leicester.)

Desford

Reid & Sigrist Ltd, Kirby Muxloe, Leicester (also advertising from Braunstone Works, Braunstone, Leicester). This company is well known for its manufacture of aircraft instruments, and also ran five Elementary Flying Training Schools for the RAF. The airfield at Desford was opened in September 1929.

Hawk XX301 is one of the thirty-nine examples that were built by British Aerospace at Bitteswell. (Author)

The Nipper Mk III has remained a popular choice for home-building due to its compact design and excellent handling. (Author)

A 1946 advertisement for the Reid & Sigrist Desford trainer.

The company's first aircraft design was the three-seat, twin-engine R.S.1 'Snargasher' trainer, G-AEOD, which was designed at New Malden and first flown in the spring of 1939. Activities at Desford during the Second World War included responsibility within the Civilian Repair Organisation for the repair and modification of Boulton Paul Defiant, Bell Airacobra (small numbers) and the North American Mitchell (seventy-two aircraft during 1944). More than 700 Defiants were to pass through Desford, with the last example leaving Desford on 30 June 1945. The first Mitchells arrived on 9 April 1943, with the last aircraft departing on 16 November 1945. (Data from Roy Bonser's *Aviation in Leicestershire and Rutland*.)

The second Reid & Sigrist design to fly was another twin-engine wooden training aircraft, the R.S.3 Desford. The construction of the main structural components (fuselage, wings and tail unit) was sub-contracted to a furniture manufacturer, the **Austin Veneer Co.** of London. The sole example, G-AGOS, first flew on 9 July 1945 and was later converted to the R.S.4 Bobsleigh for prone pilot experimentation, flying in this form on 13 June 1951. The R.S.4 received the RAF serial VZ728 whilst conducting prone pilot trials, and is now preserved in the Leicester Museum of Science & Technology.

The Desford was originally advertised as follows: 'For complete flying training the DESFORD sets a new world standard in light aeroplanes. [...] Two unique features are interconnected flaps and throttle controls, and pneumatic engine rpm indicators.'

The airfield and associated buildings at Desford were sold in 1953.

Only a single example of the graceful Desford trainer was built. This aircraft was later converted to the Bobsleigh in support of prone pilot research. (Ken Ellis collection)

The Reid & Sigrist R.S.4 Bobsleigh, VZ728 was a modification of R.S.3 Desford G-AGOS for prone pilot trials. This eventually led to the modification of Armstrong Whitworth-built Meteor F.8 WK935 to prone pilot configuration. (Ken Ellis collection)

Vickers-Armstrongs Ltd: Supermarine Spitfire aircraft were assembled at Desford from dispersed production facilities controlled by Castle Bromwich. The Desford facility was known as No.8 Factory and operated from late 1940 until September 1945. Roy Bonser in *Aviation in Leicestershire and Rutland* lists 210 aircraft that are known to have been assembled at Desford, and suggests that the total may have been as high as 1,000 aircraft, covering marks including the Mk IIa, Vb, Vc, IX and XVI.

Alex Henshaw (the famous air racing pilot and test pilot at Castle Bromwich) was responsible for the flight test of at least 150 of these aircraft. Alex Henshaw reports in *Sigh for a Merlin* that the dispersed units at Cosford and Desford began production around December 1940. It is not clear which particular aircraft (other than the 210 listed by Roy Bonser) were built at Desford, but Henshaw mentions problems during the testing of EP353, whilst this aircraft was being test-flown from Desford.

Leicester

A number of companies in Leicester were involved in dispersed manufacture for the aircraft industry during the Second World War, a selection being summarised below (see also Coalville).

H. Flude & Co. Ltd, hosiery factory on Rugby Road: Supermarine Spitfire undercarriage components.

Freeman, Hardy & Willis: Avro Lancaster main instrument panels and floors.

Leicester Bus Garage, of Briton Road, built Avro Lancaster nose, outer wing and centre fuselage sections.

Leicester Corporation Bus and Tram Depot, Abbey Park Road, manufactured Avro Lancaster ailerons and trailing edge sections, and fuselage components.

Payne's Garage, Watling Street: tool room supporting local manufacture of Supermarine Spitfire undercarriage components.

A.S. Yates, hosiery factory on Blackbird Road: chromium plating of locally produced Supermarine Spitfire undercarriage components.

Loughborough

Airwork Ltd carried out Boston and Havoc repair and modification work at Loughborough during the Second World War. The company's main base was at Heston.

Brush Electrical Engineering Co. Ltd, Falcon Works, Loughborough. The Brush company dates back to the early 1880s and its early products included generators, transformers, lighting systems, locomotives and buses. By March 1915, the company was seeking recruits for aircraft work.

The first production type was the Maurice Farman S.7 Longhorn, which was produced from 1915. Ninety-two aircraft were ordered from Brush of which at least sixty-two were built. A further twenty-five were assembled from spare parts originally manufactured by Robey & Co. Ltd, and The Phoenix Dynamo Manufacturing Co. Ltd of Bradford, to whom Brush supplied manufacturing drawings. Note that whilst *British Military Aircraft Serials 1878-1987* lists twelve examples of the Maurice Farman S.11 Shorthorn as being built by Brush, with serial numbers from 3001-3012, there is photographic evidence in A.P. Jarram's *Brush*

Brush Electrical Engineering Co. Ltd built twenty Short 827 floatplanes before commencing large-scale production of the Short 184. (Terry C. Treadwell and Alan C. Wood)

Aircraft Production at Loughborough that 3001 was actually an S.7 Longhorn. This batch of aircraft is therefore included in the S.7 total given above.

After the Longhorn, Brush built the Avro 504 in various forms, a total of 400 Avro 504 A/C/J/K being constructed. The Avro 504C version was a single-seat fighter for the RNAS, as distinct from the normal two-seat trainer configuration. A single, unsuccessful, Henry Farman Astral twin-engine bomber was built in 1916 with serial number 9251. The Longhorn and Avro 504 aircraft were flown from Loughborough Meadows close by the factory. Twenty Short 827 were built in 1916-17 for RNAS use. These aircraft were followed by 142 Short 184, out of contracts for 240. The last of these aircraft was built in April 1919. Brush Electrical Engineering Co. Ltd built a total of 651 aircraft between 1915 and 1919.

Brush purchased the non-aviation interests of Petters Ltd in 1938, and moved this (engine) business wholesale to Loughborough.

Brush Coachworks Ltd: Some 335 Dominie (military de Havilland DH89A) were built by Brush Coachworks from March 1943 out of total contracts for 455. The last Brush-built aircraft TX319 was built in 1946. These aircraft were test-flown from Loughborough Aerodrome, Derby Road, which has now been developed for housing. Other Second World War contracts included repair contracts on Hampden fuselages (ninety-nine aircraft) and Lancaster wing sections. These repair contracts were sub-contracted from the Derby Locomotive Works.

After the war, Brush reverted to locomotive production. The Falcon Works and Brush Electrical remain very much in business on the same site, running next to the railway line between the A60, and the Stanford on Soar road.

HG691 was built by Brush Coachworks at Loughborough and is seen at the RAeS Centennial of Flight Garden Party at Old Warden in June 2003. (Author)

Loughborough Cabinet Co. is identified by Barry Abraham as a sub-contractor to **Lawrence & Co. Ltd** of Nottingham, manufacturing Horsa flaps and ailerons.

Willowbrook Coachworks of Loughborough participated with Brush Coachworks in the repair of Handley Page Hampden aircraft, taking responsibility for the tail sections of these aircraft.

Wright & Sons, Quorn Mills, near Loughborough. Although listed as an aircraft manufacturer in *The Aviation Pocket-Book 1919-20*, this company manufactured a range of products used in aircraft, mainly textile items such as seat straps, parachute webbing, and braids used for glider towing. The company, whose products have been purchased by the military since the Boer War, still exists on its original site, and is still owned by the same family. No company records exist, however, prior to 1927 and it is therefore possible that some aircraft component manufacture did take place here. During the Second World War, the workforce increased to no less than 5,000 employees.

Melton Mowbray

The **Midland Woodworking Co.** (part of **Boulton & Paul Ltd**) manufactured 620 Horsa front fuselage sections at Melton Mowbray during the Second World War (see also Norwich, Norfolk).

Ratcliffe

The first aircraft to be built by **Taylorcraft Aeroplanes (England) Ltd** was Taylorcraft Plus C G-AFNW, which was flown at Ratcliffe on 3 May 1939. This was a licence-built version

A post-war photograph of Taylorcraft Plus C G-AFUA. Taylorcraft Plus C aircraft were test-flown from the airfield at Ratcliffe. (John Collier collection)

of the American Taylorcraft Model B, from which it differed as a result of a number of structural modifications, including spar dimensions and tube gauges. These differences were responsible for the distinguishing designation Plus C for British-built examples. At the time of the formation of the company *Flight* reported that the intention was to manufacture components at Thurmaston, with assembly and test-flying at Ratcliffe.

Ratcliffe was the private landing ground of the brewer, Sir Lindsay Everard. The airfield was officially opened on 6 September 1930, offering a landing area of sixty-three acres and excellent approaches in all directions.

During the Second World War, Ratcliffe was used as the base for No.6 Ferry Pilots Pool of the Air Transport Auxiliary. Pilots based there were mainly engaged on the delivery of Spitfire and Lancaster aircraft from Castle Bromwich, together with the following types: Whitley and Lancaster (from Armstrong Whitworth at Baginton); Oxford (Standard Motors, Ansty); Defiant (Boulton Paul, Wolverhampton); Stirling (Austin Motors Ltd, Elmdon).

Rearsby

Taylorcraft Aeroplanes (England) Ltd used Rearsby for the wartime test-flying of aircraft built at Syston and Thurmaston, which see for further details. The airfield initially came into use to support the Hurricane (later Typhoon) repair facility that was managed by Taylorcraft Aeroplanes (England). Once it was available, Auster aircraft were brought to Rearsby by road from Syston for assembly and test, as were repaired Tiger Moths from Thurmaston and Syston.

Auster Aircraft Ltd was formed on 8 March 1946, having previously been Taylorcraft Aeroplanes (England) Ltd. The announcement of the company's change of name read as follows: 'The manufacturers of the famous AUSTER aircraft take pleasure in announcing

G-AHAU shows the extensive modifications made to many Austers for utility operations. Built as an Autocrat, it is now almost a Husky. (Author)

that the present name of Taylorcraft Aeroplanes (England) Ltd has been changed to Auster Aircraft Ltd.'

The most successful of the post-war British light aircraft manufacturers, Auster's market was eventually cut off by the ready availability of US designs such as the Cessna 150 and 172, and the Piper Tri-Pacer, once import restrictions from the US were lifted. The Auster was a somewhat basic aircraft, by the standards of modern general aviation. It was, however, well liked, rugged and hard working, and a thoroughly practical aircraft for its time. It proved to be reliable and adaptable, with many conversions for glider towing and agricultural use, and today has an enthusiastic type club, The International Auster Club, dedicated to keeping these fine aircraft flying.

The main types built by Taylorcraft Aeroplanes (England) Ltd and Auster Aircraft Ltd are tabulated below (see also Thurmaston). The sequence chosen reflects the alphabetical/numerical model number. Note that this does not result in a chronological sequence, with new models of several types (for example, Aiglet, Autocar, Aiglet Trainer being developed in parallel). In some cases, other production numbers can be found.

Model	Date	Comments
Taylorcraft Plus C	1939	Twenty-three aircraft built pre-war under licence at Thurmaston; 55hp Lycoming O-145-A2 engine.
Taylorcraft Plus C/2	1940	Fourteen impressed Taylorcraft Plus C aircraft were subsequently converted for military use as Taylorcraft Plus C/2 with 90hp Blackburn Cirrus Minor I.
Taylorcraft Model D, Auster I (Model D/1) & Taylorcraft Plus D	1939	Nine civilian machines (Model D) followed by 100 Auster I for Army co-operation duties (Model D/1). Powered by 90hp Blackburn Cirrus Minor 1 engine. Civilianised machines known as Taylorcraft Plus D.

Model	Date	Comments
Model E Auster II	1942	Two aircraft only, subsequently converted to Auster III; 125hp Lycoming O-290-3 engine.
Model F Auster III	1942	458 built (although production total of 469 also quoted); 130hp Gipsy Major I engine.
Model G Auster IV	1943	254 built; 130hp Lycoming O-290-3 engine.
Model J Auster V	1943	Developed Mk IV. 806 built (although a production total of 790 is also quoted). 130hp Lycoming O-290-3/1 engine. Large numbers converted to civil use
Model J Auster 5C & Auster 5D	1950	Gipsy Major 1 powered variant of Auster V. Single Auster 5C G-ALKI, and some twenty-five Auster 5D.
Model J Auster 5 Alpha	1956	New-build post-war civil Auster V. Fourteen in total.
J/1 Autocrat	1946	Prototype G-AFWN, Cirrus Minor engine. 414 built – the most successful civil Auster. 100hp Blackburn Cirrus Minor 2 engine.
J/1B Aiglet	1949	Gipsy Major 1 powered, prototype G-AJUW. Eighty-six built, some eighty of which were exported, many to Australia or New Zealand.
J/1N Alpha	1955	Gipsy Major 1 variant of the Autocrat, similar to the J/1B Aiglet. Initially conversions from J/1, and subsequently forty-three new-build aircraft, plus one aircraft built from spare parts.
J/1S Autocrat	1962	One-off conversion of an Autocrat (G-AMVN) to be powered by 145hp Gipsy Major 10-2.
J/1U Workmaster	1958	G-APKP first flown 22 February 1958, developed for Crop Culture Aerial at Bembridge for agricultural use. Ten built, powered by 180hp Lycoming O-360-A engine.

The most numerous of the civilian Auster designs was the J/1 Autocrat, a three-seat aircraft powered by a 90hp Blackburn Cirrus Minor engine. F-PAGD and G-AIGD were photographed at Eggesford in Devon. (Author)

G-AMKU is a rare British-registered Auster J/1B Aiglet. Less than 100 of which were built, many being exported to Australia or New Zealand. (Author)

The Workmaster was originally designed for crop spraying and is similar to the later, and more refined, Beagle Husky. (Author)

Model	Date	Comments
J/1W Autocrat	1958	Autocrat with 180hp Lycoming O-360 engine and Workmaster tail surfaces. One aircraft only, G-25-6, effectively a lead-in to the D5 series.
J/2 Arrow	1946	Continental C75 powered two-seater, forty-five built, of which four were converted subsequently to J/4. The concept for this aircraft was effectively proven by G-AGPS, which was a one-off prototype flown in 1945 with 65hp O-145-B3 Lycoming engine. This aircraft was not formally given a designation, although it was informally known as the 'Sharp Special'. The J/2 Arrow prototype Z-1/G-AICA flew in September 1946 powered by a 75hp Continental C-75-12 engine.
J/3 Atom	1946	One aircraft G-AHSY subsequently converted to J/4 G-AJYX. 65hp Continental C-65.
J/4	1946	J/2 with Cirrus Minor 1, twenty-six built, prototype G-AIGZ. Known as Archer in Australia.
J/5	1947	Known as Adventurer in Australia. Powered by 130hp Gipsy Major 1 engine. Fifty-nine built, mostly for export, many to Australia. Similar to the J/1B and J/1N, but without the larger fin and aerodynamically balanced rudder of these types. Prototype (J/5A) G-AJER converted from J/1.
J/5B Autocar	1949	Prototype G-AJYK first flown in August 1949. Four-seater with raised rear fuselage powered by a Gipsy Major 1 engine. Eighty-two built.
J/5E Autocar	1950	Single example (G-AJYS) for racing, powered by 155hp Cirrus Major 3 engine.

The Auster J/4 is essentially an Auster J/2 with 90hp Cirrus Minor engine. The small rear quarter window distinguishes this type externally from the three-seat J/1 Autocrat. (John Collier collection)

The four-seat Autocar featured an enlarged rear fuselage. PH-NEH was photographed at the 2003 International Auster Club fly-in at Eggesford. (Author)

Model	Date	Comments
J/5F Aiglet Trainer	1951	The prototype of this clipped wing version of the Aiglet was G-AMKF/G-25-1, flying 2 June 1951. Ninety-two built powered by Gipsy Major 1 engine.
J/5G Autocar	1951	155hp Cirrus Major 3 engine, prototype G-AMKG flown July 1951. Ninety-four built.
J/5K Aiglet Trainer	1954	Two J/5K (155hp Cirrus Major 3 engine) G-AMMS, G-AMYI. G-AMYI converted to J/8L.
J/5L Aiglet Trainer	1954	Twenty-seven J/5L (145hp Gipsy Major 10-1 or 10-2 engine).
J/5P Autocar	1954	145 hp Gipsy Major 10-2 engine, prototype G-ANXZ, twenty-four built.
J/5Q Alpine	1955	Aiglet Trainer fuselage married to Autocar wings, with Aiglet Trainer aileron system. Powered by 130hp Gipsy Major 1 engine. Four built.
J/5R Alpine	1956	As J/5Q, but with 145hp Gipsy Major 10-1 engine. One conversion from J/5L; six new build; and one further aircraft completed as J/5L.
J/5T	1957	Single example G-25-4, powered by 108hp Lycoming O-235 engine. Effectively a lead-in to the D4.
J/5V Autocar	1960	A single example based on the Autocar with J/1U Workmaster fin and 160hp Lycoming O-360-B2B engine. G-APUW, first flown on 23 September 1959. Similar to the later D6, but with wooden, rather than metal wing spars.
J/8L Aiglet Trainer	1954	J/5K G-AMYI converted to be powered by a 145hp Gipsy Major 10-1/3 engine.
Model K AOP. Mk 6; Model Q T.7	1945	383 Auster AOP. Mk 6, eighty-three Auster T. 7 powered by 145hp Gipsy Major 7 engine. These included 310 AOP. Mk 6 and seventy-six T.7 for the RAF, with a further thirty-six AOP. Mk 6

Representative of the more highly developed marks of Auster, G-ANXC is a rare J/5R Alpine. This is the first of the type, converted from a J/5L. (Author)

WE563 was the first of two Auster C.4 (MK7 Antarctic) for use in the Antarctic. (Auster Aircraft Ltd via Ken Ellis)

Auster N VL522 was one of two prototypes built to compete with the Scottish Aviation Prestwick Pioneer – a British clone of the Fieseler Storch. (BAE SYSTEMS plc)

Model	Date	Comments
		and six T.7 supplied to the RCAF. Ten AOP. Mk 6 converted to T.7 standard as Auster T.10. The AOP. Mk 6 also served with the air forces of South Africa, Belgium (twenty two), Iraq, Jordan and Australia.
Auster 6A Tugmaster	1960	Glider towing civilianisation of AOP. Mk 6, initially (G-ARDX) by Air Tows Ltd at Lasham. Twenty-nine converted, powered by Gipsy Major 10-1/1. Other conversions made overseas (Canada, Belgium, South Africa, Australia).
Auster 6/Beagle A.61/1 Terrier 1	1961	Improved Auster 6A. Prototype G-ARLH first flew on 13 April 1961. Eighteen converted.
Beagle A.61/2 Terrier 2	1962	Refined version of Terrier 1, with a number of changes including increased maximum flap angle, improved ailerons and enlarged tail surfaces. Externally distinguishable by hydraulically damped tailwheel. Forty-five converted. The first A.61 Terrier 2 G-ARRN was flown for the first time on 21 April 1962.
Beagle A.61/2 Terrier 3	1969	Single aircraft G-AVYK converted by BEA apprentices and powered by 160hp Lycoming O-360-B2B engine.
Model M	1945	Project study and mock-up against Specification A.2/45.
Model N	1946	Two aircraft only (VL522 & VL523) designed to meet Specification A.2/45 and powered by 250hp Gipsy Queen 32 engine. VL522 was first flown on 28 April 1948.
Model P Avis	1947	Four seat, four door design shown as Z-2 at Radlett 1947. Subsequently registered as G-AJXW and modified in 1948 to become the Avis 2 G-AJYF. Powered by Gipsy Major 10 engine.

Above: *The first four-seat Auster Avis Z-2 at the 1947 SBAC show at Radlett. The type did not enter production.* (John Collier collection)

Right: *The Auster B4 Ambulance/Freighter under construction in the experimental hangar at Rearsby.* (IAC Heritage Group)

Model	Date	Comments
Model S	1951	WJ316 (modified from Mk 6 VX125) was a private venture design intended for use as a light observation post. The Model S eventually led to the successful Auster AOP. Mk 9. Powered by 180hp Bombardier 702 engine.
B4 Ambulance/ Freighter	1951	Single example G-AMKL with rear loading doors and tail boom. First flight 7 September 1951. Powered by 180hp Bombardier 702 engine.
B5 AOP. Mk 9		Prototype WZ662 first flown 19 March 1954. 167 built, powered by 172hp Bombardier 203 engine.

The angular and rugged Auster AOP. Mk 9 was the last of the military Austers. This example was photographed at Eggesford in Devon. (Author)

The Auster B.8 Agricola was a specialist agricultural aircraft. Eight were completed, the type being used almost exclusively in New Zealand. (John Collier collection)

Model	Date	Comments
B8 Agricola	1955	Specialist agricultural aircraft. Prototype G-25-3 first flown 8 December 1955. Eight built.
C4 Mk 7 Antarctic	1955	Two T.7 aircraft – WE563, WE600 – for Antarctic Survey use.
C6 Atlantic	1957	Four-seat touring aircraft with tricycle undercarriage. Single example G-25-5/G-APHT powered by 185hp Continental E-185-10 engine.Not flown.
D4/108	1960	The prototype D4/108 G-25-8/CS-AME flew on 12 February 1960. Six built at Rearsby, with additional parts for nine aircraft for assembly in Portugal. Powered by 108hp Lycoming O-235-C1 engine.
D5/160	1960	Prototype was flown on 10 January 1960. Twenty-five at Rearsby, with additional parts for a further 141 aircraft to be assembled in Portugal. Powered by 160hp Lycoming O-320-A engine.
D5/180	1962	Two built at Rearsby and five by OGMA. Production continued as Beagle D5/180 Husky, fourteen of which were built, see Beagle below.
D6/160, D6/180	1960	Lycoming-powered Autocar derivatives. One 160hp aircraft G-25-1 /LN-BWB and three D.6/180.

In 1957, perhaps more in hope than expectation, Auster were advertising their new design, the Atlantic as 'setting new standards of styling, comfort and flying ease. Modern nose-wheel undercarriage, spacious air-conditioned cabin'.

During the 1950s and '60s, the company also produced components for other manufacturers, including parts for the de Havilland Dove and Boulton Paul Balliol, and a range of

G-ARLG is a pristine D4/108, a type built under licence in Portugal. (Author)

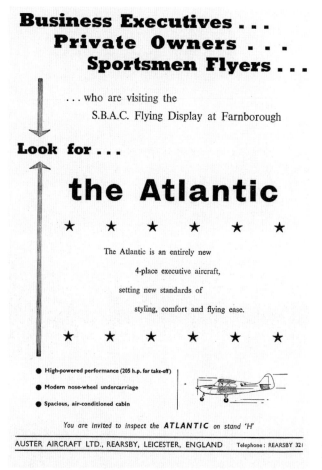
A 1957 advertisement for the Auster Atlantic by Auster Aircraft Ltd.

items for Hunting Percival for use on the Prince, Sea Prince and Pembroke. Auster also produced car components, this part of the business continuing to operate as Rearsby Automotive after Beagle had taken over.

Taylorcraft Aeroplanes (England) Ltd, and Auster Aircraft Ltd constructed around 3,600 aircraft in addition to their notable wartime repair activities at a number of sites in the area.

Beagle–Auster Aircraft Ltd: On 7 September 1960, Auster Aircraft Ltd was taken over by the Pressed Steel Co. Ltd and became Beagle-Auster Aircraft Ltd. The main product of this period was the A.61 Terrier civil conversion based on the Auster AOP. Mk 6, T.7 and T.10. These aircraft were ex-RAF aircraft bought back by the manufacturer and stored either at Kidlington or at Broome Lane, Rearsby. Production details are included in the preceding table.

From 1962, the company was known as **Beagle Aircraft Ltd**. The last production machine flown at Rearsby was the four-seat Beagle A.109 Airedale, whose prototype G-25-1/G-ARKE first flew on 16 April 1961. Forty-three Airedale were built between April 1961 and August 1964. The single Beagle E.3, or AOP. Mk 11, G-ASCC was an Auster AOP. Mk 9 development, powered by a 260hp Rolls-Royce IO-470-D Continental engine. G-ASCC was first flown as G-25-12 on 18 August 1961, and later carried military marks as XP254.

The company also produced the Beagle D5/180 (or A.113) Husky, a final development of the Auster line. This rugged STOL aircraft was powered by the 180hp Lycoming O-360-A2A engine. A total of fourteen were built.

Beagle A.61 Terrier 2 G-ASOM was one of a number of conversions of ex-military Austers, in this case from AOP. Mk 6 VF505. (Author)

The Beagle A.109 Airedale was a four-seater with tricycle undercarriage and swept fin, but could not compete with imported American designs of similar configuration. (Author)

Above: *G-ATMH is a Beagle-Auster D5/180 Husky, the last of the hard-working line of Auster utility aircraft.* (Author)

Right: *The front fuselage assembly rig for production of the Beagle 206 at Rearsby.* (IAC Heritage Group)

After 1964, Beagle at Shoreham concentrated on development activity of the B.121 Pup and the Beagle 206. Once the Beagle 206 design had reached production status, this was undertaken at Rearsby. Similarly, B.121 Pup development was undertaken at Shoreham, with the Rearsby factory contributing wings and tail units. At this time (1968) the aircraft were assembled at Shoreham and then returned to Rearsby for final paint and finish. By January 1969, the Pup had transitioned to full production at Rearsby. The design and support rights to Auster Aircraft Ltd were sold to Hants & Sussex Aviation Ltd in 1968.

A hangar packed with Beagle Pup fuselages in full production at Rearsby. (IAC Heritage Group)

A wartime photograph of Auster III fuselage production at Syston. (IAC Heritage Group)

Syston (north east of Leicester)

The Taylorcraft/Auster concern made use of production facilities at Syston for the manufacture of their designs prior to a concentration of activity at Rearsby. The facilities at Broad Street, Syston eventually became the machine shop for both the aeronautical and automobile business. See also Rearsby and Thurmaston.

G-AHCR is a Taylorcraft Plus D (Auster 1) built in 1942. It has been re-engined with a Continental C90 to become the sole Gould Taylorcraft Plus D Special. (Author)

Thurmaston (north east of Leicester)

Taylorcraft Aeroplanes (England) Ltd was set up by A.L. Wykes, (Chairman) with co-directors P. Wykes and F. Bates, the company being registered on 21 November 1938. The company initially built an Anglicised version of the Taylorcraft Model C (later named Plus C), before moving on to construct aircraft of its own design. Mr Wykes was the Managing Director of Crowther Ltd of the Britannia Works, Thurmaston, the works being used for the manufacture of textile machinery. Taylorcraft Aeroplanes (England) Ltd set up its own factory at the rear of these works.

The first Taylorcraft Plus C G-AFNW was flown from Ratcliffe in April 1939, although the company subsequently used Rearsby for flight test purposes. Twenty-three Taylorcraft Plus C were built prior to the outbreak of the Second World War. Fourteen impressed aircraft were subsequently converted for military use as Taylorcraft Plus C/2 with 90hp Blackburn Cirrus Minor I engines.

Taylorcraft Aeroplanes (England) Ltd went on to manufacture the Taylorcraft Model D and its developments. The Model D was a more powerful machine with a 90hp Cirrus Minor engine replacing the 55hp Lycoming O-145 of the Plus C. Nine civilian Taylorcraft Model D were followed by 100 Army co-operation Model D/1 Auster AOP. Mk I. In civil use, the type is known as the Taylorcraft Plus D.

Production of Auster types for the RAF is reported (*International Auster Club News*, Vol.24, No.2) as 100 AOP. Mk I, two Auster AOP. Mk II (subsequently converted to AOP. Mk III), 458 AOP. Mk III, 254 AOP. Mk IV, and 790 AOP. Mk V. To these wartime aircraft can be added the later AOP aircraft constructed by **Auster Aircraft Ltd** (see Rearsby).

Taylorcraft Aeroplanes (England) Ltd was responsible for a very significant wartime activity encompassing, in addition to the repair of 300 of the company's own Auster designs, 368 Hurricane, 281 Typhoon, 339 Tiger Moth, a single de Havilland Hornet Moth and eleven Kirby Cadet gliders. Ten dispersed sites were in operation in 1942, including Syston,

Auster 5A TW511 (G-APAF) photographed at Henstridge in a wartime AOP colour scheme, despite having been built post-war for the civil market. (Author)

Taylorcraft Aeroplanes (England) Ltd was an important repair centre during the Second World War responsible for Auster, Tiger Moth, Hurricane and Typhoon repairs. (John Collier collection)

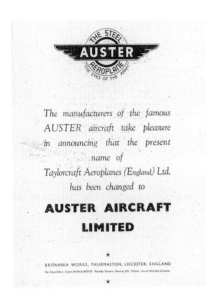

An advertisement from March 1946 announcing the formation of Auster Aircraft Ltd, formerly Taylorcraft Aeroplanes (England) Ltd.

Mountsorrel, Thurmaston and Rearsby. Taylorcraft also manufactured components for such types as the Oxford, Hurricane, Spitfire, Tiger Moth and Albemarle. The company was advertising in January 1946: 'Taylorcraft Auster, The Steel Aeroplane. "The Eyes of the Army".'

Wymeswold

Burgoyne-Stirling Dicer: this aircraft flew with the 'unofficial' registration G-AECN from RAF Wymeswold before moving in 1950 to Burton-on-the-Wolds. For details, refer to the entry for Knowle/Honiley in Warwickshire.

Field Aircraft Services Ltd made use of Wymeswold from the late 1950s for aircraft overhauls and major servicing work, moving to Wymeswold from Tollerton. The main work carried out involved overhaul and repair of RCAF aircraft based in Europe, including the Avro Canada CF-100, Canadair CT-33 Silver Star and the F-86 Sabre. Similar work was subsequently carried out for the USAF and US Navy on C-54 and R5D-1 aircraft. Field Aircraft Services were also active in civil overhaul work, handling a wide range of types, including the Vickers Viking and Viscount; Douglas DC-3, DC-4, DC-6, and DC-7; and Miles Marathon. The company also operated at Croydon and Bovingdon, and moved to Castle Donington in 1968.

Wymeswold was temporarily used for **Rolls-Royce Ltd** flight test activity from January 1955 to February 1956 due to runway re-surfacing at Hucknall. Types included: Hunter and Canberra (Avon trials), and two Ashton test beds (WE670 with Avon RA14 mounted underfuselage, and 'Conway' Ashton WB491).

Lincolnshire

Bracebridge Heath (near Lincoln)

Bracebridge Heath was used as **No.4 Aircraft Acceptance Park** (AAP) during the First World War because of the large-scale production in the Lincoln area. Robey & Co. Ltd constructed an aerodrome for its own use at Bracebridge Heath in 1916. This aerodrome was also used for the test-flying of Sopwith types built by Clayton & Shuttleworth Ltd. The site was taken over by the War Office in late 1916 and then enlarged significantly, including the construction of seven 'Belfast'-roofed, brick-walled hangars in 1917. The AAP completed its move to Bracebridge Heath in 1919, having been initially sited (from 1915) on Lincoln West Common (part of Lincoln Racecourse). During the Second World War the site was taken over and used by the A.V. Roe & Co. Ltd Repair Organisation.

A.V. Roe & Co. Ltd used Bracebridge Heath, along with Langar, as an overhaul and repair facility – initially of the Avro Manchester, but mainly of Lancaster aircraft; the Anson and York were also subject to repair and modification here. During the Second World War, the A.V. Roe & Co. Ltd Repair Organisation returned more than 4,000 aircraft to service. The organisation made use of nearby RAF Waddington for flying, the aircraft being moved from Bracebridge Heath to Waddington by road.

The capabilities of the Langar and Bracebridge Heath sites are summed up in the following advertising copy from September 1947:

> *Originating as wartime servicing stations for Lancasters, Langar and Bracebridge have now become even more the centre of Avro's 'after sales service' policy. At Langar and Bracebridge today, aircraft of any make are welcome, and a large, technically qualified staff is always ready to carry out any sort of maintenance and repair – from swinging the compass to a complete overhaul of both engines and airframe. For 'after sales service', buy Avro, but even if you don't – come to Avro for servicing, just the same!*

Nine Lancaster aircraft were converted at Bracebridge Heath for Egyptian use in 1950, carrying markings of G-11-60 to G-11-68. Four Lancaster freighter conversions (with Lancastrian noses) were completed for BSAA in 1946. Lancaster I PD328 was modified for long-range and Arctic navigation trials in 1944, carrying the name *Aries*. The Repair Organisation was responsible for repair and modification of the Avro York and Avro Lincoln, and modified three Lancaster aircraft to take part in the film *The Dam Busters*. Bracebridge Heath was also used for component/spare part production and supported a number of Hawker Siddeley in-service types in this way, including the Gloster Meteor and Armstrong Whitworth Argosy, as well as the Avro 748, Shackleton and Vulcan. Two Avro 707 aircraft (WZ744 707C, and WZ736 707A) were completed at Bracebridge Heath and flown from

Avro 707A WZ736 was one of five sub-scale test aircraft supporting the Vulcan programme. WZ736 was built at Bracebridge Heath and first flown at RAF Waddington. (Author)

RAF Waddington. Avro 707A WD280 was also modified here, being provided with a revised wing planform. Bracebridge Heath passed into **British Aerospace** hands in the 1970s, and although now closed, the hangars are still extant.

Cranwell

Cranwell Light Aeroplane Club produced a series of light aircraft designs, under the direction of Flt Lt Nicholas Comper who was, at the time, an engineering lecturer at Cranwell. The CLA.2 was designed by Comper for the 1924 Lympne Light Aeroplane Trials and first flew at Cranwell on 14 September 1924. The CLA.2 was a lightly built and under-powered biplane which, but for its side-by-side seating, had the superficial appearance of a relatively crude Hawker Cygnet. During the trials, the CLA.2 managed to fly a distance of 762.5 miles in 17 hours 53 minutes – a stately 42.6mph – to win the endurance prize of £300. The CLA.2 was later registered as G-EBKC.

The CLA.3, G-EBMC, was produced for the 1925 Lympne trials and was a diminutive parasol monoplane, with the wing passing just above the fuselage. The clean lines of the Bristol Cherub-powered CLA.3 endow the type with a clear family resemblance to the later Comper Swift.

The Cranwell CLA.4 was a clean Cygnet-like biplane, but of inverted sesquiplane config-uration, and was intended to use a Pobjoy engine – the designer of which, D.R. Pobjoy, was an Education Officer at Cranwell. The fact that Comper and Pobjoy both taught at Cranwell goes a long way to explain Comper's use of the Pobjoy engine for the Swift and the estab-lishment of the Pobjoy factory alongside that of Comper at Hooton Park. Sadly, Pobjoy, like Comper, died tragically, being killed in an accident whilst travelling as a passenger in a civilian DC-2. Two CLA.4 were built, G-EBPB and G-EBPC (CLA.4A), both being intended entrants for the 1926 Light Aeroplane Competition at Lympne. In the event, only the first aircraft took part and, although eliminated from the trial, G-EBPB (flown by Flt Lt Comper) won the Stewards' Handicap race at 70.85mph on 17 September 1926. The Cranwell Light Aeroplane Club was disbanded in 1927.

Gloster Aircraft Co. Ltd: The first flights of the first two jet aircraft types to be designed by Gloster were carried out at Cranwell, these being:

- Britain's first jet aircraft, the experimental E.28/39 W4041/G, first flown on 15 May 1941, piloted by P.E.G. 'Gerry' Sayer.
- F.9/40 'Rampage' (later to be named Meteor) DG206/G, first flown on 5 March 1943, piloted by Michael Daunt. DG206/G was, in fact, the fifth F.9/40 to be built, but engine problems prevented the other prototypes flying ahead of this example, which made use of the de Havilland H.1 engine, later to be developed into the Goblin.

Gainsborough, Lincolnshire

Marshall & Sons of Gainsborough built at least eighty-three of an order for 150 Sunbeam Arab-powered Bristol F.2B Fighter, the first aircraft being D2626. One aircraft was also built up from spares, additional to the contract. Aircraft were tested at Lincoln West Common aerodrome (part of Lincoln racecourse).

Hemswell (east of Gainsborough, Lincolnshire)

The **Shield** Xyla was built as a school project to the design of Mr George Shield (Grammar School, Maple Road, Mexborough). The only example, G-AWPN, was first flown on

G-AWPN is the sole example of the Shield Xyla, construction having been undertaken as a school project. (Author)

30 October 1971 and is still flying more than thirty years later. The Xyla is a wooden, open-cockpit, single-seater, reminiscent of a single-seat Druine Turbi (or an enlarged Turbulent). G-AWPN was damaged in a ground loop at Finmere in 1980 and spent a period in storage, prior to a major rebuild, which commenced in 1997. The fully restored aircraft flew again from Deanland on 23 June 1999.

Lincoln

Clayton & Shuttleworth Ltd built forty-six Sopwith Triplane from orders for 146, the first being N5350, delivered on 2 December 1916; forty-six Handley Page O/400 from an order for fifty; at least 550 (possibly 577) Sopwith Camel from total orders for 650, the first being B5651; and three Vickers Vimy from an order for 150, the remainder being cancelled.

Clayton & Shuttleworth of Lincoln were major contractors for Sopwith aircraft, including this Camel, B7276 which is preserved in the Canadian National Aeronautical Collection, Ottawa. (J.S. Smith)

(Sopwith production figures are taken from *Sopwith – The Man and His Aircraft*. Note that *Aircraft Made in Lincoln*, on the other hand, gives forty-nine Triplane from orders for 155, and 582 Camel from orders for 650.) The company constructed parts for Sea Scout Airships prior to beginning work on Sopwith Triplane production.

The works were a farm machinery and steam engine factory, The Stamp End Works, sited on Waterside North, next to the River Witham. Other works used for aircraft construction included the Titanic Works (Sopwith Triplane and Camel), and the Abbey Works and Tower Works (Handley Page O/400).

Clayton & Shuttleworth-built aircraft were test-flown at the Robey aerodrome at Bracebridge Heath, which became the No.4 (Lincoln) Aircraft Acceptance Park (AAP) in 1919. The O/400s were flown to the AAP directly from a field next to the Abbey and Tower Works that is still known as the Handley Page Field.

A member of the same Shuttleworth family, Richard Ormonde Shuttleworth, established the Shuttleworth Collection (now The Shuttleworth Trust) at Old Warden, Bedfordshire, the UK's premier collection of airworthy vintage and veteran aircraft.

Robey & Co. Ltd built a wide range of types, including thirty Sopwith Admiralty 806 Gunbus, thirteen of which were delivered as spares; some 256 Short 184; the Maurice Farman Longhorn; and the Robey-Peters RRF.25 Gun Machine. The first aircraft to be built was Sopwith 806 No.3833 in mid-1915. Longhorn production included seventeen aircraft (N5000 to N5016) from an order for thirty, with additional parts supplied for assembly by Brush Electrical at Loughborough.

The first aircraft were built at Robey's Coultham Street Works, the later machines being built in a shed behind the Canwick Road Works. Initially aircraft were taken to Lincoln West Common aerodrome (on the racecourse), but in 1916 Robey & Co. Ltd established an aerodrome close to Bracebridge Heath for test-flying.

The RRF.25 was first flown in September 1916 and was distinguished by having a pilot and two gunners (each of the gunners being provided with wing mounted 'pulpits' to maximise their field of fire). Two RRF.25 were constructed, but the project was abandoned. The first example 9498 crashed on its second flight and the second example 9499 crashed on its first flight on 8 April 1917.

The company went into receivership in 1968 and was purchased from the receivers by Hadfield & Co. Ltd, who renamed it Robey of Lincoln Ltd. Although the Robey title remains (with Beel Industrial Boilers Plc), the operating company went out of existence some years ago. Some company records are held with Lincolnshire County Archives.

Ruston, Proctor & Co. Ltd of 46 Queen Victoria Street, Lincoln (offices) constructed the following types:

- 200 Royal Aircraft Factory BE2, made up of 100 BE2C, thirty-one BE2D and sixty-nine BE2E. The first aircraft to be built by the company was BE2C 2670.
- 350 Sopwith 1½ Strutter (in four batches, the first aircraft 7762 being delivered on 11 July 1916, and the last B2600 being delivered on 25 July 1917). A number of the 1½ Strutter aircraft were delivered to allied forces, including those of France, Belgium, and Russia. High production rates were achieved, that of the 1½ Strutter peaking at forty-three per month.
- 1,573 Sopwith Camel (from orders for 1,575, although 1,625 is also quoted). The first Camel was B2301, completed on 1 June 1917. Peak production rate for the Camel was 128 per month in May 1918. The 1,000th Sopwith Camel to be constructed (B7380) was painted in a particularly striking special paint scheme to celebrate this achievement. Some of the late production Camel aircraft were delivered directly to store at Ascot without engines.

Robey & Co. Ltd of Lincoln were the most important contractors for the Short 184, building 226 from the total production of 926 aircraft, production being split between ten companies. (Terry C. Treadwell and Alan C. Wood)

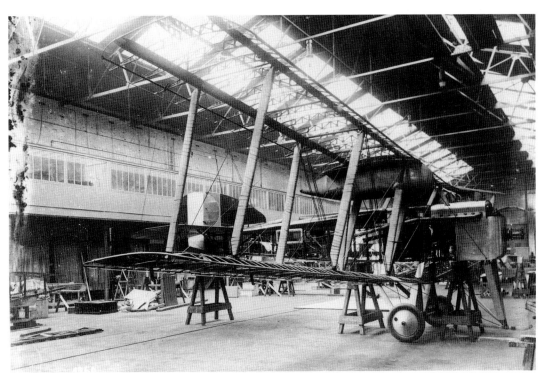

The second Robey-Peters three-seat fighting machine being assembled. (Ray Hooley collection)

The BE2C 2699, preserved in the Imperial War Museum, was built by Ruston, Proctor & Co. Ltd of Lincoln. (J.S. Smith)

- Some 500 Sopwith Snipe from orders shared with Portholme Aerodrome Ltd. The first Snipe E7337 was delivered in October 1918. A number of the Snipe aircraft were delivered to Portholme Aerodrome Ltd for completion at Oddfellow's Hall, Thetford. The peak Snipe production rate was eighty-four per month in January 1919. *Aircraft Made in Lincoln* indicates that 462 Snipe of an order for 500 were completed in Lincoln, with the last thirty-eight being sent to Thetford for completion. Of the next batch, fourteen aircraft were sent to Thetford for completion, and eleven were delivered directly to store at Waddon without engines.

To sustain this level of aircraft production, the company constructed new works at Boultham by the River Witham and Spike Island. Like the other companies in the area, aircraft were initially tested at No.4 AAP at Lincoln West Common, with later production machines being tested at Bracebridge Heath.

Ruston, Proctor & Co. Ltd had their origins in the manufacture of traction engines, threshing machines and excavators. The company was renamed **Ruston & Hornsby Ltd** on 11 September 1918 and offered all their stock for sale in February 1919. All aircraft built after the formation of Ruston & Hornsby carried that name on their manufacturer's construction plate. In March 1919, Ruston & Hornsby were reported to have manufactured 2,750 complete aircraft and 4,000 aero engines and equivalent parts during the war. The engines manufactured by Ruston, Proctor & Co. Ltd included the Clerget 9Z and 9B, the Bentley BR2 rotary and the ABC Dragonfly radial engine. Car manufacturing by Ruston & Hornsby after the First World War proved an unsuccessful venture.

Lincoln West Common Racecourse

West Common racecourse was used as No.4 AAP from 1915, conducting acceptance trials of Ruston-built machines and aircraft from other local firms. After the War Office took over

The Ward Gnome G-AXEI is Britain's smallest aircraft. (J.S. Smith)

Bracebridge Heath in 1916, acceptance trials were also undertaken there, the AAP moving completely to Bracebridge Heath in 1919.

North Scarle, Lincolnshire

The **Ward** Gnome G-AXEI was built at North Scarle by its designer and first flew at Wigsley on 4 August 1967. The Gnome is the UK's smallest aircraft with a span of 15ft 9in, and a length of only 11ft 6in.

The P.45 Gnome was followed by the Ward E.47 Elf, which was later registered as a micro-light, G-MMUL. The Elf had a span of 15ft 10in, and a length of 11ft 10in and attained a stately maximum speed of 45 knots using a 600cc Citroen engine. This aircraft was completed in 1982, but did not make its first 'hop' until 7 April 1984 at East Kirkby. Both the Gnome and the Elf were constructed in a workshop measuring only 8ft 6in by 6ft 6ins. The main-wheels of the Elf are a pair of Spitfire tailwheels.

RAF Scampton (near Lincoln)

Hawker Siddeley Aviation Ltd used RAF Scampton for flight tests of RAF F-4 Phantom fleet following the closure of Holme-on-Spalding Moor in 1983.

RAF Waddington (near Lincoln)

A.V. Roe & Co. Ltd: The Avro 707A WZ736 first flew at RAF Waddington on 20 February 1953, Avro 707C WZ744 following on 1 July 1953, both aircraft having been assembled at Bracebridge Heath. During the Second World War, aircraft subject to repair and modification by the the A.V. Roe & Co. Ltd Repair Organisation at Bracebridge Heath were also test-flown from RAF Waddington, where a hangar was retained for assembly and flight test.

The Bircham Beetle was largely an amalgam of various aircraft parts. It is not clear whether the Beetle was actually flown. (Ken Ellis collection)

Norfolk

Bircham Newton

The **Bircham** Beetle was a diminutive low-wing monoplane of ungainly appearance, which was built at RAF Bircham Newton in 1924. Various available components, including the cut-down rudder of an Avro 504 and the rear fuselage of a Bristol F.2B Fighter, were combined with a Douglas engine and a wing of original design. Whereas it is suggested (for example in Ken Ellis' *British Homebuilt Aircraft Since 1920*) that the wing may have been derived from a Fokker D VII, Ord-Hume suggests, convincingly, that it must have been of original design. The aircraft was un-registered, and its inclusion here reflects the view that it may have flown in 1924, rather than any definite information or evidence that it did so.

Great Yarmouth

R.S. Watling & Sons of The Maltings, Great Yarmouth, is listed in *The Aviation Pocket-Book 1919-20* as an aeroplane manufacturer with propeller branch. Nothing else is known.

King's Lynn

Savages Ltd of King's Lynn and Stroud manufactured seventy-three Beardmore-powered AIRCO DH1A (source: Gunston – *World Encyclopaedia of Aircraft Manufacturers*), fifty Voisin LA, 121 Avro 504K, and 100 AIRCO DH6 from 1915 to 1918.

Norwich

Boulton & Paul Ltd (of Chapelfield Works; Riverside Works; Rose Lane Works; and Mousehold Aerodrome) was established in 1897 in Norwich and was to become one of Britain's major aircraft manufacturers. The company telegraphic address was 'Aviation, Norwich'.

Having its origins in an ironmongers founded in 1797 by William Moore, Boulton & Paul Ltd became a diversified business manufacturing a large range of wood and engineering products. The company's aircraft department was set up in 1915. In 1934, the aircraft business was split off and renamed (on 30 June 1934) **Boulton Paul Aircraft Ltd**, moving to Wolverhampton in July 1936. The non-aircraft products of Boulton & Paul Ltd were described (*The Aeroplane*) in February 1935 as 'buildings from the greatest houses to the largest aeroplane hangars. The World's biggest producers of wire netting'. Other products included portable bungalows, chicken runs, sheds and hangars.

Boulton & Paul's first aircraft production comprised fifty Royal Aircraft Factory FE2B ordered in June 1915; the first aircraft (serial 5201) was flown on 2 October 1915. At the time that this first aircraft was flown, *Flight* described Boulton & Paul as the 'well-known boat-builders' of Norwich. The final production figures for the FE2 were around 250 FE2B (some sources state 225), and 300 FE2D. All the FE2D nacelles were built by Richard Garrett & Sons of Leiston, who then went over to building the FE2B themselves. These aircraft were flown at Mousehold Aerodrome, which had previously been a cavalry drill ground.

In October 1915, the company purchased fourteen acres of land on the far side of the River Wensum from J.J. Colman Ltd, and this became the Riverside Works, production starting there in April 1916. In addition to aircraft construction, Boulton & Paul had a separate propeller branch, which manufactured 7,835 propellers during the First World War.

Boulton & Paul's major production effort switched from the FE2 to the Sopwith Camel, the company building 1,575 (some sources state 1,550) aircraft in only fifty-seven weeks. The highest rate achieved was some seventy aircraft in a single week. Boulton & Paul and the Lincoln-based Ruston, Proctor & Co. Ltd each built nearly three times as many Camel aircraft as The Sopwith Aviation Co. Ltd themselves. The last First World War production by Boulton & Paul was of the Sopwith Snipe, around 420 being built of 500 ordered. Seventy Felixstowe F.3 and F.5 hulls were also built, but 150 Vimy ordered from Boulton & Paul were cancelled.

Boulton & Paul set up its own design capability in 1917 under Mr J.D. North. Mr North was highly experienced, having worked for the Aeronautical Syndicate Ltd, following which

A Boulton & Paul-built FE2B 7666 that has come to grief in a garden. (Terry C. Treadwell and Alan C. Wood)

The P.9 entered limited production, a total of eight being built, but the market was not yet ready for the sale of large numbers of private aircraft. (Boulton Paul Association)

he became Chief Engineer for Grahame-White at Hendon (where he was the designer of the Grahame-White Charabanc, among other types). From 1915 to 1917, Mr North was the Superintendent of the Aviation Department of Austin Motors.

The design activity had, initially, only limited success. The company built a single example of the P.3 Bobolink fighter C8655, which was flown in January 1918. Boulton & Paul also built a single P.6 biplane (X25) for experimental work, and an enlarged version of the P.6, the P.9. An unregistered prototype and seven production P.9 were built. The P.10 was an early example of all-metal construction.

During the inter-war years, a number of types were built in small numbers and flown at Mousehold, examples including:

- P.25 Bugle J6984, first flown July 1923.
- P.31 Bittern twin-engine monoplane fighter of 1927 – two prototypes, the first being J7936, flown in February 1927.
- P.33 Partridge, competitor to the Bulldog for F.9/26. One only, J8549, flown in January 1929.
- P.64 Mailplane G-ABYK, first flown March 1933.
- P.71A (G-ACOX, G-ACOY), a development of the P.64 for passenger use, which flew in 1934.

Although only two P.71A were built, the advertising was glowing: 'Luxurious – Speedy – Safe. The Boulton Paul P.71A cruises at 165 mph with up to 14 passengers. Lands or takes off in less than 200 yards. Twin-engine security, metal construction.'

AIRCRAFT IN THE MAKING—No. 6

*Being one of a series of announcements which describe
and illustrate interesting Scientific Devices, Instruments
and Machinery utilised in the designing and making of
B. & P. Aircraft.*

METAL CONSTRUCTION

Messrs. Boulton & Paul have been foremost in the development
of steel construction for Aircraft.

Special machines, some of which are illustrated here, have been
designed and laid down after two years of careful research.
They are now able to supply aeroplanes in which wood is
entirely eliminated.

The first of these models—the P. 10—was exhibited at the
recent Paris Aerial Locomotive Exhibition and met an
enthusiastic reception.

*"The P. 10 probably marks the greatest step forward in aeroplane
construction of any machine in the show."—FLIGHT.*

*"The most advanced example of constructional thought in the whole
show."—AEROPLANE.*

NORWICH

London Office Address: 135-137, QUEEN VICTORIA STREET, E.C. 4.
Tel. No.: 4642 Central. Teleg.: "BOUTIQUE, CENTRAL, LONDON."

Write for particulars of P9, the real Commercial Aeroplane.

*Boulton & Paul's pioneering use of metal construction is promoted in this advertisement from February 1920
featuring the Boulton & Paul P.10.*

Consistency and Reliability in the King's Cup Race

TWO Boulton & Paul low horse-powered machines were entered. Both completed the course, averaging the speed declared by the makers, the second machine finished six minutes behind the first in a trip of 800 miles.

This accomplishment justifies the consistent reliability claimed by

BOULTON & PAUL, LIMITED

for their commercial and fighting Aircraft.

**ALL STEEL
DAY AND NIGHT BOMBERS
a Speciality.**

Enquiries from Foreign Governments solicited.

Designers and Makers of Aircraft.

Boulton & Paul Ltd.

HEAD OFFICES AND WORKS: NORWICH.

Telephone: Norwich 851.   Telegrams: "Boulton, Norwich."

London Office Address: 135-137, Queen Victoria Street, E.C.4.

Left: *An advertisement publicising the performance of two P.9s in the first King's Cup air race in 1922.*

Below: *The Boulton & Paul P.32 J9950 was an imposing three-engine bomber designed to meet specification B.22/27. Only a single example was built, this being flown for the first time during 1931. (Ken Ellis collection)*

The unique configuration of the P.64 Mailplane is shown to perfection in this air to air photograph. Although antiquated to modern eyes, it was as fast as the fighters of the day. (Boulton Paul Association)

LUXURIOUS · SPEEDY · SAFE

The Boulton Paul P.71A cruises at 165 m.p.h. with up to 14 passengers. Lands or takes off in less than 200 yards. Twin engine security. Metal construction. Write for details.

BOULTON PAUL AIRCRAFT LTD.
NORWICH ● ENGLAND

Boulton Paul Aircraft's P.71A in 1935. The change in company name from Boulton & Paul Ltd reflects the creation of a separate aircraft business on 30 June 1934.

The Boulton & Paul's Sidestrand medium bomber was a successful and popular type, not least for its excellent handling characteristics. (Ken Ellis collection)

The most successful Boulton & Paul designs of this period were the P.29 Sidestrand of 1926 (prototype J7938), and the closely related Overstrand of 1934. The Sidestrand, despite its inelegant appearance, proved to be an excellent bombing platform and was strong and remarkable manoeuvrable, being fully capable of being rolled, looped and spun. Twenty Sidestrand were constructed, five of which were later converted to Overstrand. The Overstrand was fitted with a nose-mounted gun turret, and was the first RAF type to be so equipped – something of a harbinger for one of Boulton & Paul's most important product lines in the Second World War. The Overstrand prototype was a conversion of Sidestrand J9179 and was first flown on 3 February 1934. The prototype was followed by twenty-four production machines.

In 1936, Boulton Paul was advertising: 'The Boulton Paul Overstrand – The 24 hour bomber. The first service type to be fitted with mechanically operated gun turret.'

A lesser-known type was the diminutive P.41 Phoenix of 1929. This was a two-seat parasol monoplane G-AAIT, distinguished by its 'all-flying' elevator. The Phoenix was initially powered by an ABC Scorpion, being subsequently extensively revised, and re-engined with a Salmson radial.

As pioneers of metal construction, Boulton & Paul built spars and complete wings for a number of other companies, examples including production for the Saro London, and the Blackburn Shark, B2, and Bluebird IV. The company was also responsible for the manufacture of the longitudinal girders for the airship R101.

As was common at the time, Boulton & Paul were keen to remind potential customers of their prowess in metal construction, advertising in 1930: 'Boulton & Paul Ltd. Designers and Makers of all-metal aircraft. Contractors to the Air Ministry; the Admiralty; the War Office; HM Board of Works; the Crown Agent to the Colonies; English, South American and Indian Railways; Sudan, South African and Egyptian Governments.'

Boulton & Paul/Boulton Paul Aircraft Ltd built a total of 2,628 aircraft at Norwich. At the time of its move to Wolverhampton, Boulton Paul Aircraft Ltd was part way through production of 106 Hawker Demon aircraft, fifty-nine of which were completed at Norwich, and forty-seven at Wolverhampton.

During the Second World War, the Norwich branch of Boulton & Paul Ltd became once again involved in aircraft production, building components for Oxford aircraft and Horsa gliders. The works were bombed, however, and this work was transferred to another member of the Boulton & Paul group, **Midland Woodworking Co**. at Melton Mowbray.

Mann, Egerton & Co. Ltd of Norwich are known today as major car dealers and distributors. The firm was established in 1899 at 5 Prince of Wales Road, Norwich, their origins being indicated by their telegraphic address: 'Motors, Norwich'. Like many others in the motor industry, Mann, Egerton & Co. Ltd undertook aircraft contracts during the First World War, advertising in November 1915 as 'Manufacturers of aircraft and component parts. Contractors to the Admiralty and HM War Office. Motor Engineers and specialists in coachwork. 150 new and second-hand cars always in stock.' Other slogans from 1916 to 1917 included 'Our Norwich Works are specially constructed and organised for the scientific design and manufacture of up-to-date seaplanes and aeroplanes in large quantities' and 'Manufacturers of Proved Efficiency of all Types of Aircraft'.

The Norwich premises extended to 10,000sq.ft and the company ran two additional factories, one of which was built in only nine weeks. Sixty acres of land were purchased at Aylsham Road and laid down as an aerodrome.

The Chief Designer was Mr J.W. Carr, previously of Deperdussin at Paris and Brooklands. Production is summarised below:

- Short 184: Twelve built.
- Mann, Egerton Type B: Ten examples of an improved version of the Short 184.
- Short 225 Bomber: Twenty aircraft.
- Sopwith 1½ Strutter: Seventy-five aircraft.

The Mann, Egerton Type B was an improved version of the Short 184 and ten were built. (Terry C. Treadwell and Alan C. Wood)

Mann, Egerton & Co. Ltd built seventy-five Sopwith 1½ Strutter at their Norwich factory.
(BAE SYSTEMS plc)

Mann, Egerton & Co. Ltd built 123 SPAD VII fighters, of which B9913 survives and is preserved in the Canadian
National Aeronautical Collection, Ottawa. (J.S. Smith)

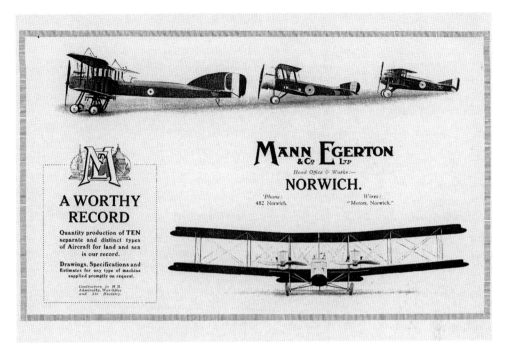

The proud record of Mann, Egerton & Co. Ltd during the First World War.

- SPAD VII: One example (serial 9611) was used as a pattern, allowing Mann, Egerton to build a further 123 aircraft.
- AIRCO DH9: 100 aircraft.
- AIRCO DH9A: at least 150 aircraft.
- AIRCO DH10A: at least twenty-one, and possibly as many as thirty-two aircraft, from an order for seventy-five.
- Single examples of the company's own designs, the H.1 (serial N44), and H.2 Type N1a Seaboat Scout (N45).

In 1919 the company was advertising 'Quantity production of TEN separate and distinct types of aircraft for land and sea is our record'. As is indicated above, a total of at least 500 aircraft were built, fully justifying this claim.

Trevor, Page & Co., of Exchange Street, Norwich, is listed as an aeroplane manufacturer with propeller branch in *The Aviation Pocket-Book 1919-20*; nothing else is known.

The **No.3 Aircraft Acceptance Park** was established at Mousehold in November 1917 to handle East Anglian aircraft production.

Reymerston Hall, Norfolk

Wallis Autogyros Ltd: Although never reaching true production status, Wg Cdr Ken Wallis has built a series of outstandingly successful gyroplanes at Reymerston Hall. The capability of these machines is demonstrated by the large number of world records that they held, including, for a long period, all of the absolute world records for autogyros. The Wallis WA116 Agile G-ARZB is perhaps the world's most famous autogyro as a result of its starring role in the James Bond film *You Only Live Twice*. G-BLIK, which has the complex designation WA-116/F/S, was used to break a number of speed and distance records in the 1980s.

Capabilities demonstrated by various examples of the breed include: altitude, 18,976ft; distance in a straight line, 543 miles; distance in a closed circuit, 623 miles; speed over 3km, 120mph; duration, 6 hours 25 minutes. In all, a total of thirty-two separate world records have been recognised by the FAI in Class E3 (all autogyros) and Class E3a (autogyros below 500kg all-up weight). Some twenty-one Wallis autogyros of all types have been built, including a small batch laid down by Beagle at Shoreham. Some of the first flight dates of individual Wallis autogyros are as follows: WA118 Meteorite G-ATPW, 6 May 1966; WA117 G-AVJV, 28 May 1967; the same aircraft rebuilt as G-AVJW, 9 August 1969; and WA121 G-BAHH, 28 December 1972.

Right: *G-ARZB is the most famous of the Ken Wallis series of record-breaking autogyros due to its starring role in the James Bond film* You Only Live Twice. (Author)

Below: *Wing Cdr. Ken Wallis with his Wallbro monoplane replica G-BFIP, which was flown at RAF Swanton Morley in 1978.* (Ian J.E. Hancock)

Ken Wallis has also built a modern replica of a monoplane built in 1909 by his father and uncle, known as the 'Wallbro' Monoplane. The 'Wallbro' (**Wall**is **bro**thers) Monoplane was 'hopped' in 1910 at Fulbourn, near Cambridge, before being damaged beyond repair in a storm that destroyed its hangar in October 1910. The Wallis brothers founded a company to promote the type, this being the **Wallis Aeroplane Co.**, of 12 St Barnabas Road, Cambridge. The Wallis Wallbro replica G-BFIP was first flown on 10 August 1978 from RAF Swanton Morley, powered by a 72hp McCulloch engine.

Thetford

Portholme Aerodrome Ltd completed a number of Sopwith Snipe aircraft delivered by Ruston, Proctor Ltd, this work being conducted at Oddfellow's Hall, Thetford. The aircraft involved included E7798 to E7836 and H351 to H364.

Northamptonshire

Hinton in the Hedges

The **Cliff Piper** Métisse home-built light aircraft G-BVCP was first flown from Hinton in the Hedges on 19 December 1999. The aircraft's name is the French word for *mongrel*, this reflecting the use of a number of existing components in the construction of the aircraft. These include a Nipper wing (mounted low-set, unlike the shoulder-wing location of the Nipper), Sonerai undercarriage and Colibri canopy. The aircraft is powered by a Revmaster engine and flight tests have shown a maximum cruising speed of 110 knots and stalling speed of approximately 38 knots. Early test-flying has shown the need to increase the height of the fin and rudder to improve directional stability.

The Métisse home-built aircraft marries a Tipsy Nipper wing to a new fuselage design. The type was first flown from Hinton in the Hedges on 19 December 1999. (C.W.R. Piper)

Northampton (see also Sywell Aerodrome)

J. Radley and W.B.R. Moorehouse were trading as **Portholme Aerodrome Ltd** from registered offices at 16 Guildhall Road, Northampton. For further details of Portholme Aerodrome Ltd, see Huntingdon, Cambridgeshire.

Sywell (Northampton Airport)

Sir W.G. Armstrong Whitworth Aircraft Ltd: Plans were made in February 1941 for the manufacture of the Whitley bomber at Sywell. In the event, two hangars were erected, but the Whitley order was cancelled. The facilities were, however, used by Sir W.G. Armstrong Whitworth Ltd for the final assembly and flight test of some of the 300 Avro Lancaster Mk II bombers constructed by this firm. The number completed at Sywell is not clear, however, with Christopher Paul stating in *Sywell – The Story of an English Aerodrome 1928-78* that it was 'nearly one hundred aircraft'. The same source indicates that the first machine to fly from Sywell did so on 31 July 1942, and the last on 25 November 1943. The fuselage and centre section was locally built at the **Corporation Tram Sheds**, Northampton; the tail surfaces at **Pearce's Shoe Factory**; and the wings by the parent company at Baginton. After the end of the Second World War, the hangars used were absorbed into the capacity of Brooklands Aviation Ltd as their number 4 site (see below).

C. Boddington built a BE2C replica G-AWYI at Sywell in 1969, using a number of Tiger Moth components. This aircraft was subsequently exported to the USA.

During the Second World War, **Brooklands Aviation Ltd** ran a Wellington repair organisation at Sywell; 1,841 aircraft were repaired here between mid-1940 and 1945. Alex Henshaw reports in *Sigh for a Merlin* that the Castle Bromwich flight test department test-flew seventy-one Wellington aircraft that had been repaired by Brooklands Aviation Ltd at Castle Bromwich, and a further 180 at Sywell. The repair activity was supported by a number of local companies, which carried out work on components and major assemblies under the direction of Brooklands Aviation Ltd. In addition to the facility at Sywell, Brooklands opened a second site nearby at Moulton that carried out repair work on Wellington fuselages and engine nacelles. The somewhat unglamorous postal address was Brooklands Aviation Ltd, Number 2 Site, Buttocks Booth, Moulton, Northants. A third site (on Sywell airfield) carried out engine repair work. Christopher Paul in *Sywell* states that the first aircraft to be repaired was L4349, with the last being RP329.

After the Second World War, Brooklands Aviation Ltd was responsible for a range of overhaul and modification work for the RAF, types worked on including: Wellington (overhaul); Dakota (servicing and overhaul during the Berlin Air Lift); Mosquito (overhaul and conversions from B.35 to TT.35 configuration); and Varsity (support work from 1957 until 1971). The Mosquito conversion work was underway in the early 1950s, as evidenced by the conversion of TA719 and RS712 in August and November 1951, respectively, and TA634 in 1952. In November 1954, the company was advertising vacancies, as follows: 'Airframe fitters urgently required for production and repair of jet aircraft'. This was associated with a contract for overhaul of the de Havilland Vampire, this work being transferred in due course to Little Staughton, where there was a hard runway available. A limited number of **de Havilland** Venom FB.1 were built by Brooklands Aviation Ltd (either at Sywell or Little Staughton), including WE469, WK395, and WK423-425.

Jetstream Aircraft Ltd: This company was formed in September 1970 (by Capt. Bill Bright of Terravia Trading, and Scottish Aviation Ltd), to complete the production of incomplete Handley Page Jetstream airframes. **Terravia Trading Services Ltd** acquired the rights to the

Jetstream design in March 1970. After re-naming as Jetstream Aircraft Ltd, the company moved to Leavesden. Subsequently all production rights were acquired by **Scottish Aviation Ltd** at Prestwick. The development of the Jetstream was originally undertaken by Handley Page Ltd at Radlett, Hertfordshire. The type was further developed by British Aerospace at Prestwick.

Nottinghamshire

Gamston Airfield (near Worksop)

Ivan Shaw's Europa prototype G-YURO first flew at Gamston on 12 September 1992. The **Europa Aircraft Co.** latterly, **Europa Management (International) Ltd**, of Kirkbymoorside, North Yorkshire, manufacture the type in the form of kits for home assembly. The Europa has become one of Britain's most successful post-war light aircraft.

Hucknall

This entry covers Rolls-Royce engine test activity, which has been a long-standing and dominant feature at Hucknall, followed by an alphabetical listing of other aircraft types flown here. Hucknall was a First World War airfield, and an RAF station during the inter-war period.

Rolls-Royce Ltd engine testing: Rolls-Royce Ltd have been present at Hucknall continuously for seventy years, and a wide range of sometimes unusual aircraft have been used at Hucknall in support of engine test and development activities. The Rolls-Royce Ltd test fleet of three aircraft – Hart, Fury and Gnatsnapper – moved to Hucknall from Tollerton in 1934. (Reference: *The Magic of a Name*, Harold Nockholds.) Gloster Gnatsnapper III N227 was used for Goshawk and Kestrel IIS trials, before being relegated to use as a hack aircraft.

Hawker Horsley aircraft were extensively used in support of engine testing, including the Condor IIIB, Eagle, H.10, Buzzard, Leopard III, Jumo and Rolls-Royce PV12 (Merlin C, E, F, G) engine testing. Individual aircraft used included J7511 (the prototype), J8003, J8611 (Merlin), J8620 (Leopard, Jumo), J8932, S1436 (Merlin C) and S1452 (Condor III). The Merlin I was first flown in a Horsley test bed on 20 December 1935.

Hart aircraft were used in support of both Kestrel and PV12/Merlin. Examples include G-ABMR which was flown with twelve different Kestrel variants, K1102 in support of the Kestrel V, and K3036, which, after flying at Brooklands on 21 February 1935, was flown with the PV12, and Merlin C, E and F. The Hawker High Speed Fury K3586 (first flown at Brooklands on 3 May 1933) was flown with the Kestrel IIS, S, IIIS, VIS, Goshawk III, B.41 and PV12. The Hawker PV3 (a larger and uprated Fury, flown at Brooklands on 15 June 1937) was flown with three different Goshawk variants, and delivered to Rolls-Royce Ltd in October 1935. The first flight of the PV12 was in a Hawker Hart on 12 April 1935.

In 1936 Rolls-Royce Ltd purchased a Heinkel He 70G G-ADZF for Kestrel and Peregrine development, allowing testing of these and other engines in a representatively clean monoplane. The Heinkel also allowed development of ancillary systems such as radiator installations, propellers, oil coolers and exhaust systems.

The test-flying of the Merlin in the second-line Hawker types outlined above was followed by intensive development of the Merlin and Griffon in a range of operational types. The first Merlin-powered Whitley, K7208, was flown from Hucknall on 11 February 1938. Important work was carried out in support of the two-speed, two-stage supercharger for the Merlin 61. The Supermarine Spitfire III prototype N3297 was used to develop this engine, and first flew at Hucknall with the Merlin 61 on 20 September 1941. Spitfire Vc AB196 and AB197 were also deployed on this task. This development directly led to the Spitfire IX, which was able to claw back superiority over the Focke Wulf Fw 190 at a critical phase of the air war. Wellington II T2545 was retained here to assist in the development of the Merlin 60.

Rolls-Royce Ltd converted a number of Hurricane aircraft to Merlin XX power as the Hurricane IIA, the total number of aircraft involved being variously reported as forty or 100. The company also undertook Hurricane repair work. The first three North American Mustang aircraft to be converted to Merlin power were flown at Hucknall.

Bristol Beaufighter development included the Merlin Beaufighter II R2058, first flown in July 1940. Two Beaufighter II prototypes were later used at Hucknall as Merlin 61 test beds. Another Beaufighter engine test bed was the comparatively little known Griffon IIB-powered Beaufighter IIF (T3177).

The Hawker Henley prototype K5115 was used as a flying test bed for the Rolls-Royce Vulture from 1939 to produce one of the most unprepossessing aircraft of the Second World War. Other Henley test bed aircraft included L3302 in 1940, and L3414, which flew with a Griffon II installation in support of Firefly I development.

Avro Lancaster test aircraft for piston engine development included: ND784/G Merlin 85 installation testing for the Avro Lincoln; R5849 Merlin 600 annular cowlings; JB675 inboard Merlin 621 for Tudor I, outboard Merlin 620 for Argonaut; and PP791 Merlin 600. Lancastrian VM704 tested two Griffon 57 inboard for the Shackleton, with two Merlin T.24/4 outboard for the Tudor. A second Lancastrian VM728 was also flown in this configuration.

The flight-testing of jet engines was carried out at Church Broughton to the west of Derby. The Trent Meteor, the world's first turboprop aircraft, first flew at Church Broughton on 20 September 1945. By 1944 there were forty-eight aircraft of fourteen different types operating from these test locations.

Examples of turbine engine test bed aircraft, many of which operated from Hucknall and Church Broughton, include:

Type	Test bed Fleet
Derwent	Wellington, first flown December 1943.
(developed	Meteor 4 RA430 and RA435 were used for Derwent development.
Rover W.2B/26)	Afterburner development made use of Meteor 4 RA435 and VT196 (after-burner tests 1949-53, including Derwent 5 port and Derwent 8 starboard).
	Avro Lincoln SX971 (modified by AST Ltd and flown in October 1950, after-burner equipped Derwent mounted beneath fuselage).
	Meteor FR.9 VZ608 was used for afterburner and thrust reversal trials using the Derwent 8 and was first flown at Hucknall on 19 October 1951. This aircraft was subsequently modified for trials of the RB108 lift engine, see below.
Nene	First flight at Hucknall in Lockheed YP-80A 44-83027 on 21 July 1945.
	Lancastrian VH742 (first flown 14 August 1946), and VH737.
	Vampire aircraft as follows: TG276, TG279, TG280, and TX807.
	Tudor 8 VX195 first flown September 1948.
	Viking VX856 first flown at Wisley on 6 April 1948.
	Canberra VN813.
Trent	Meteor Mk I EE227, first flown 20 September 1945.
Dart	Lancaster NG465, first flown on 10 October 1947 and carried out 800 hours of Dart testing.
	DC-3 KJ829, G-ALXN, G-AMDB.
	Wellington LN715.
	Ambassador G-AKRD/G-37-3, 1961.
Avon	Lancastrian VM732 first flown August 1948 (Avon RA.2, 3), VL970 (Avon RA.3, 7, 9, 14).

The Avro Tudor 8 VX195 was a conversion of Tudor I G-AGST/TT181 to four-jet configuration for test purposes. The Tudor 8 was first flown in this form on 6 September 1948. (BAE SYSTEMS plc)

Type	Test bed Fleet
Avon	Avro Lincoln RA716 (previously used for Theseus trials) modified with two Avon in 1955.
	Meteor F.4 RA491 was used for Avon RA.2, RA.3 testing, flying from Hucknall on 29 April 1949.
	Several Hunter aircraft including WT560, WT565, WT573, XE530, XE531, XE532.
	Canberra B2 WD943 afterburner trials.
	Ashton WB491.
Clyde	Wyvern VP120, 18 January 1949.
Tay	Viscount VX217, first flown 15 March 1950.
RB108	Meteor VZ608 was modified to have an RB108 lift engine fitted in the centre fuselage, the conversion being carried out by F.G. Miles Ltd at Shoreham in 1955. VZ608 first flew with the RB108 fitted on 18 May 1956 at RAF Tangmere.
Soar	Meteor F.8 WA982, first flown with a wing tip mounted Soar installed on 25 February 1954.
Tyne	Avro Lincoln RF533, mid 1956 as G-37-1.
	Ambassador G-37-4/G-ALZR 1957, G-37-3/G-AKRD August 1958.
Conway	Vulcan VX770 (R.Co.7), XA902 (R.Co.11).
	Ashton WB491 (R.Co.12 for Boeing 707-420).

Viscount VX217 was used for test-flying of the Rolls-Royce Tay engine, flying for the first time in this form on 15 March 1950. VX217 was subsequently used by Boulton Paul Aircraft Ltd for the development of electrically signalled flight controls. (Alec Brew)

Gloster Meteor VZ608 was fitted with a Rolls-Royce RB108 lift engine in the centre fuselage, the conversion work being carried out by F.G. Miles Ltd at Shoreham. (J.S. Smith)

The Rolls-Royce Thrust Measuring Rig is more commonly known as the 'Flying Bedstead'. (Author)

Type	Test bed Fleet
Spey	Vulcan XA902 flown on 12 October 1961, with Conway inboard, Spey outboard.
RB211	VC10 G-AXLR/XR809, first flown at Hucknall on 6 March 1970.

The first Rolls-Royce Thrust Measuring Rig (or Flying Bedstead) XJ314 flew at Hucknall (tethered) on 9 July 1953, and in free flight on 3 August 1954. A second rig, XK426, was also constructed and flown on 12 November 1956.

Whilst nothing remains to be seen at Church Broughton, it seems appropriate that Hucknall's long association with engine testing is continued by the present-day engine test facility that stands here like a piece of modernistic sculpture.

At the other end of the scale in size and technology, Hucknall is also the base of the superb, and appropriately registered, Hawker Cygnet replica G-CAMM. This aircraft was constructed by **Don Cashmore** and was the winner of the best replica award at the PFA Rally at Cranfield in 1994. G-CAMM first flew on 13 March 1993. Other Don Cashmore replicas include Bristol M1C C4912/G-BLWM flown at Hucknall on 21 June 1987, and Sopwith Tabloid G-BFDE/168, both of which were built for the RAF Museum.

The **Granger** Archaeopteryx was a striking tail-less design built by the brothers R.F. & I. Granger (lace makers of Nottingham) with some assistance from C.H. Latimer-Needham. The Archaeopteryx first flew at Hucknall in October 1930, but was not registered (as G-ABXL) until 1932. G-ABXL was preserved at the Shuttleworth Trust and has been flown occasionally at Old Warden. The author can attest to it being a truly remarkable sight in the air.

G-CAMM is Don Cashmore's fine Hawker Cygnet replica. (Author)

The unique tailless Granger Archaeopteryx is preserved by the Shuttleworth Trust, but rarely flown. (Author)

The Granger brothers had previously built a biplane glider known as the Linnet, which Ord-Hume reports was later fitted with an ABC engine and flown in 1926.

Rolls-Royce Ltd's flying club (the **Merlin Flying Group**) modified Auster J/4 G-AIPH to Continental O-200 power, the aircraft being flown on 6 January 1966 as G-37-5, and subsequently reverting to G-AIPH.

Fifty-four Lancasters were prepared at Langar for delivery to the Aéronavale. (BAE SYSTEMS plc)

RAF Langar

A.V. Roe & Co. Ltd overhaul and repair facility, along with Bracebridge Heath. The capabilities of the two sites are summed up in the following advertising copy from September 1947:

> *Originating as wartime servicing stations for Lancasters, Langar and Bracebridge have now become even more the centre of Avro's 'after sales service' policy. At Langar and Bracebridge today, aircraft of any make are welcome, and a large, technically qualified staff is always ready to carry out any sort of maintenance and repair – from swinging the compass to a complete overhaul of both engines and airframe. For 'after sales service', buy Avro, but even if you don't – come to Avro for servicing, just the same!*

Langar opened in 1942, and had facilities, after further expansion in 1943, covering nearly 300,000sq.ft. During the war, the Avro repair organisation returned more than 4,000 aircraft to service.

Argentine Avro Lincoln B-003 was modified at Langar with a faired nose and tail to become the Avro 695 Lincolnian, LV-ZEI. Field Aircraft Services purchased three Avro Lincoln aircraft that were stored at Langar with a view to conversion as meat freighters for Paraguay as ZP-CBP-96 to ZP-CBS-98. In the event, the scheme failed and the aircraft were scrapped. A.V. Roe & Co. Ltd modified fifty-four Lancasters at Langar for use by the Aéronavale. Later Langar was used for Shackleton overhaul and modification.

During the 1950s, RCAF Sabre aircraft used the airfield at Langar. The A.V. Roe & Co. Ltd facilities at Langar were closed by Hawker Siddeley Aviation Ltd in 1968.

Production, possibly of O/400 wing ribs, at Wm. Lawrence & Co. Ltd. The labour-intensive nature of the work and the largely female workforce are evident. (Via Lawrence Automotive)

Nottingham

The Aircraft Construction Co., Great Alfred Street, Nottingham and Harley Aeroplane Works, Beckton Road, E16: This company was formed in London by Mr R.P. Grimmer. In November 1917 it was advertising 'Ribs, spars, longerons, tanks, wiring, plates and every description of metal fitting' and 'Aeronautical Designers and Engineers. Speciality: Windscreens complete with Non-Flamoid. Every accessory and component part of any aeroplane supplied at the shortest notice'. Mr Grimmer's initial activity was aircraft parts manufacture, with the ultimate intention of complete machines.

Wm Lawrence & Co. Ltd, Vale Rd, Colwick Nottingham: This company was originally a wholesale furniture manufacturer, founded by Mr William Lawrence in 1875 and registered as a limited company in 1895. In 1899, the company moved to a large new factory at Colwick. One of their furniture advertising slogans was 'Quality is remembered long after the price is forgotten'. Their aircraft works covered no less than eight acres and held contracts for Shorts, Handley Page and Fairey Campania aircraft. Furniture production was resumed in 1919, although the aircraft building experience was put to use for a period building wooden car bodies as well as furniture. During the Second World War the company built motor launches for the Admiralty and participated with **Harris Lebus** and **Waring & Gillow** in the manufacture of Hotspur gliders. The company also manufactured a large quantity of Horsa flaps and ailerons, using **Buoyant Upholstery** of Sandiacre, Nottingham, and **Stag Cabinet Co.** (also of Nottingham) as sub-contractors.

The Colwick factory ultimately extended to eleven acres, and had its own railway siding and electricity generating station. By autumn 1996, the factory was being demolished, and houses were to be built on the site. By mid-1997, all that remained was a huge pile of bricks amid a post-industrial wasteland, shortly to become another anonymous housing development.

The **Nottingham Aircraft Manufacturing Co.** announced their move from 32 King Street to Castle Meadow Road in February 1918. Nothing else is known.

The Nottingham Monoplane was reported in *Flight* in November 1911, and was built by **Searby, Allen & Searby**, of Hartley Road, Nottingham. The machine was powered by a 30hp Alvaston engine.

Tollerton Aircraft Services Ltd re-assembled and test-flew Hampden aircraft following overhaul by **Brush Coachworks Ltd** and **Derby Locomotive Works**. The company continued performing repair and overhaul activities through the Second World War, including the repair and modification of Avro Lancaster bombers. This activity later led to the overhaul of aircraft by Field Aircraft Services Ltd (the parent company of Tollerton Aircraft Services Ltd), also at Tollerton airfield.

Rolls-Royce Ltd used Tollerton airfield for engine test-flying from 1931 until the opening of their airfield at Hucknall in 1934. One of the test fleet was Gloster Gnatsnapper N227 re-engined with a Kestrel IIS. This aircraft moved to the newly opened Hucknall at the end of February 1935.

Oxfordshire

Abingdon

The **Howitt** Monoplane G-AEXS was a parasol monoplane designed by Mr R.C. Howitt, and built at Manor Road, Garsington near Cowley, by Mr J.B. Acres. G-AEXS was flown from Abingdon in May 1937. The aircraft had a fuselage which resembled that of the de Havilland DH53, and a distinctly 'de Havilland' style of fin and rudder. Power was provided by a 600cc Douglas engine, which was later to be replaced by a 1,000cc Brough motorcycle engine.

The MG Car Co. Ltd at Abingdon produced more than 100 nose sections for the Albemarle, and also manufactured components for both the Typhoon and Tempest.

Morris Motors Ltd used Abingdon for flight-testing, after setting up the No.1 Civilian Repair Unit. Later the company rebuilt a number of Spitfire aircraft as part of the Civilian Repair Organisation, some of which were flight-tested at Abingdon. Once Cowley was available to Morris Motors as an airfield (associated with their production of the Tiger Moth), most of the Spitfires and Hurricanes repaired by the company were flown from Cowley.

Barford St John (South of Banbury)

Gloster Aircraft Co. Ltd: This airfield was briefly used for Gloster Meteor flight test activities from 1943.

The prototype Halifax made its first flight at RAF Bicester in October 1939. 6,100 were built, this example having been constructed by The English Electric Co. Ltd. (BAE SYSTEMS plc)

RAF Bicester

Halton Aero Club: The **Halton** HAC.I Mayfly G-EBOO was first flown at Bicester on 31 January 1927. This was the first of two machines built at RAF Halton technical training school in the 1920s. The Mayfly was a two-seat biplane, distinguished by its X-shaped interplane struts. C.H. Latimer-Needham, Education Officer at RAF Halton, designed the type for the 1926 Lympne Light Aircraft Competition. Unfortunately, the Mayfly was not ready in time, and the HAC.I first flew at Bicester on 31 January 1927, participating enthusiastically and successfully in a number of air races, pageants and air shows in 1927.

The Halton HAC.II Minus was a modification of the Mayfly, it being converted in 1928 from a two-seat biplane to a single-seat parasol monoplane to improve its performance. The Minus retained the same registration as the Mayfly, despite the drastic change to its configuration. The discarded wings and interplane struts were subsequently used by the Clarke Cheetah G-AAJK. Both the Mayfly and the Minus were raced successfully in the late 1920s, the Minus winning the 1928 Wakefield Trophy at a speed of 95mph.

Handley Page Ltd transported the prototype Halifax L7244 to Bicester for assembly prior to its first flight on 25 October 1939. More than 6,100 Halifax were built by the following companies: Handley Page Ltd at Radlett; The English Electric Co. Ltd at Preston/ Samlesbury; The Fairey Aviation Co. Ltd at Heaton Chapel; Rootes Securities Ltd at Speke; and the London Aircraft Production Group in a number of factories in the London area, final assembly being at Leavesden. For further details refer to these locations, the main entry being that for Radlett in *British Built Aircraft: Volume 3*.

RAF Brize Norton

The No.6 Maintenance Unit at Brize Norton was responsible for the erection of many Horsa gliders, the airfield being the home of the RAF Heavy Glider Conversion Unit.

Chalgrove Airfield

Chalgrove is the **Martin-Baker Aircraft Co. Ltd** (later Martin-Baker Ltd) test airfield, ten miles south east of Oxford. Chalgrove was the base during the late 1940s of the superlative

Martin-Baker MB5 and has for many years been the home of the much-modified Meteors used by Martin-Baker for ejection seat trials. Some 1,500 test ejections have been made from the Meteor trials fleet.

Martin-Baker have a long history of Meteor operations, starting with Meteor III EE416 which was delivered to the company at Oakley Airfield, near Thame, on 6 November 1945. Extensive modification was required to make this single-seat Meteor suitable for ejector seat trials, the seat being fitted behind the normal cockpit, in what was originally the ammunition bay. Photographic platforms used (with limited success) by Martin-Baker included Meteor III EE415 and EE338.

Other Meteor trials aircraft included T.7 WA634 (delivered to Martin-Baker on 30 January 1952, and first used for ejection trials on 31 August 1953). WA634 was fitted with the empennage of the Gloster E.1/44, thus becoming a Meteor 7/8 hybrid (sometimes referred to as a Meteor 7½). Two further similarly modified aircraft followed – WA638, and WL419. WL419 was originally used to supply spares for WA638, but was itself made airworthy in 1979 and remains in use at Chalgrove. Ground test ejections were performed in support of the development of rocket-powered seats, these making use of the wingless Meteor WA686, this being a Meteor F.8 front fuselage, fitted with a T.7 tailcone. The second prototype of the two-seat Hunter, XJ267, was delivered to Martin-Baker Ltd at Chalgrove for ejector seat development.

The first live ejection was made on 24 July 1946, when the famous and brave test subject Bernard Lynch was ejected from a Meteor. Sqn Ldr J.S. Fifield made the first live ejection from ground level at Chalgrove on 3 September 1955 from WA634. On 11 June 2003, an ejection from a Sea Harrier FA.2 brought the total number of lives saved by Martin-Baker ejection seats to 7,000. Some evidence of the necessity of ejection seats for high performance aircraft is that 10 per cent of all the ejection seats manufactured by Martin-Baker have been used in emergencies to save lives.

Chipping Norton

Folland Aircraft Ltd are reported as having dispersed capacity at Chipping Norton during the Second World War.

WL419 is one of Martin-Baker's famous Meteor 7/8 hybrid ejection seat development and trials fleet. (Martin-Baker Aircraft Ltd)

T7404 is a Morris Motors-built Tiger Moth, often flown by the author in the late 1970s. (Author)

Cowley

Morris Motors Ltd, at Cowley were chiefly involved in Tiger Moth production (3,432) and repair, and were also responsible, within the Civilian Repair Organisation, for the repair and modification of Spitfires and Hurricanes. Wartime Tiger Moth production by Morris Motors has also been quoted as 3,210 aircraft. Spitfire test-flying was carried out by the Supermarine test pilots Jeffrey Quill and Alex Henshaw. Hurricane aircraft were also repaired by Morris Motors Ltd and flown by Hawker test pilots. Alex Henshaw reports in *Sigh for a Merlin* that the Castle Bromwich flight test department test-flew 260 Spitfire aircraft that had been repaired at Cowley by No.1 CRU. Cowley was also home to the ominously entitled No.1 Metal Produce and Recovery Depot (an aircraft scrap yard and smelting unit).

East Hanney

Berkshire Aviation Co. Ltd converted five Avro 504K for civil use at East Hanney, to the south west of Oxford. These aircraft were registered G-EBCK, G-EBFV, G-EBIN, G-EBKB, and G-EBKX. Berkshire Aviation moved to Witney in 1926, converting one further aircraft there. The company was formed in August 1921 by the brothers J.D.V. Holmes and F.D.V. Holmes, who had been operating war surplus Avro 504 aircraft for pleasure flying as soon as they became available for civilian use. The company was later renamed Berkshire Aviation Tours Ltd.

Harwell (near Didcot)

Known today for its atomic research establishment, RAF Harwell was used for the first flight of the **Martin-Baker Aircraft Co. Ltd** MB2 on 3 August 1938, and the incomparable Martin-Baker MB5 R2496 on 13 May 1944. The Napier Dagger-powered MB2 featured a distinctive trousered undercarriage and small fin and rudder, looking rather similar to a grown-up Miles Sparrowhawk. The MB2 was registered G-AEZD, but was, rather confusingly, marked M-B-1 (later becoming P9594). For further details of these aircraft, see the entry for Denham in *British Built Aircraft: Volume 3*.

The Berkshire Aviation Co. Ltd converted five Avro 504 for civil use at East Hanney. The company founders (left to right) were J.D.V. Holmes, Alan Cobham, F.D.V. Holmes and R. Graham-Wollard. (Colin Cruddas)

The incomparable Martin-Baker MB5 made its first flight at Harwell in May 1944. (Martin-Baker Aircraft Ltd via Ken Ellis)

The Cierva W.9 helicopter with its innovative jet efflux torque reaction system was flown for the first time at Henley. PX203 was the sole example of the type. (Ken Ellis collection)

Henley-on-Thames

The Cierva Autogiro Co. Ltd: The Cierva W.9 helicopter PX203 was flown from Henley-on-Thames in late 1944 or early 1945, the Cierva concern being based at that time in Thames Ditton. PX203 ceased flying after being damaged in an accident in January 1948.

Vickers-Armstrongs Ltd: Henley-on-Thames was used for Supermarine Spitfire assembly and flight test of airframes constructed by dispersed production in the Reading area. Spitfire PR. IV aircraft were tested here during 1941 and 1942.

Oxford (see also Cowley and Witney)

Goodden Monoplane: This was an Antoinette-like monoplane built at Wolvercote in 1912 and which flew until 1913 at Port Meadow aerodrome. The machine was also known as the Goodden Dragonfly. Its constructor, Frank Goodden, was later test pilot for the Royal Aircraft Factory until his untimely death on 28 January 1917.

Witney

Berkshire Aviation Co. Ltd (later **Berkshire Aviation Tours Ltd**) rebuilt Avro 504K G-EBIZ at Witney after moving from East Hanney in 1926. This aircraft became the first machine of one of the best-known joy-riding concerns, Cornwall Aviation Co. Ltd, and was based at Margate. Berkshire Aviation Tours built two Avro 548 in 1931 for the use of Giro Aviation at Southport.

Chilton Aircraft Ltd used Witney for test-flying of the Chilton D.W.1 Monoplane from April 1937. The test pilot was Ranald Porteus, who was later to become well known as the demonstration pilot for Auster Aircraft Ltd. The D.W.1 was designed and built by the Hon. A. Dalrymple and A.R. Ward, and was built in the grounds of Chilton Lodge, just to the north of Hungerford, where A.R. Ward lived. Work on the type began in 1936, with **Chilton Aircraft Ltd** being formed in May 1936.

    The D.W.1 was a delightful single-seater of clean lines and sparkling performance. The Ford-engined prototype G-AESZ was fitted with a throttle that worked in the reverse sense to the norm – this provoked some comment at the time! The Chilton performed well in air

This post-war view of Witney shows three camouflaged hangars and a mixed bag of de Havilland products – Rapide, Dove, Tiger Moth and Mosquito. (BAE SYSTEMS plc)

The prototype Chilton Monoplane G-AESZ was test-flown from Witney airfield in Oxfordshire. (Author)

races, particularly with the Train and, later, Mikron engines. The Train-engined D.W.1A G-AFSV won the 1939 Folkestone Trophy at 126mph – highly creditable on 44hp. Four aircraft were completed, all of which survived the war.

A repair unit managed by **The de Havilland Aircraft Co. Ltd** was based at Witney during the Second World War. Its repair contribution was to return to service 320 Hurricane and 335 Spitfire, in addition to 905 aircraft of de Havilland design.

The **Willoughby Delta** was a two-seat, twin-engine, twin-tail boom design with a fixed undercarriage, powered by two 125hp Menasco engines and registered G-AFPX. The name Delta reflects the tapered triangular fairing between the outer wing panels and the tail booms. The crew sat in a pod at the wing centre section. The design, although unconventional in appearance, was backed up by careful wind tunnel testing, and was intended to be a sub-scale demonstrator for a larger transport aircraft. G-AFPX was constructed at Minster Lovell between Witney and Burford, and first flew in April 1939 at Witney, demonstrating remarkably good performance. Unfortunately, the prototype was destroyed in a fatal accident on 10 July 1939, and no further development took place. **The Willoughby Delta Co. Ltd**, which developed the machine, had registered offices in Moorgate, London.

Shropshire

RAF Cosford

Vickers-Armstrongs Ltd: Supermarine Spitfire assembly was carried out at Cosford from dispersed production under the control of Castle Bromwich. Alex Henshaw reports in *Sigh for a Merlin* that the dispersed units at Cosford (and Desford) began production around December 1940. It is not clear how many aircraft were built at Cosford, but, in the same source, Henshaw mentions problems during test flights of EP499 and EP510, both aircraft being flown from Cosford in 1942. Four hundred and seventy Spitfires had tropical modifications implemented at Cosford for service in the Middle East.

RAF Cosford is now the site of an important branch of the RAF Museum with a notable collection of British-built experimental prototypes and transport aircraft.

RAF Shawbury

North American Aviation used two hangars at Shawbury until June 1940 for the assembly of Harvard aircraft, prior to this work being taken over by Helliwells Ltd at Walsall and (later) Rootes Securities at Blythe Bridge.

These facilities were then used by **Rootes Securities Ltd** for the assembly of Blenheims from components manufactured at Speke, being known as No.9 Factory.

The factory passed to the control of **Vickers–Armstrongs Ltd** on 18 February 1943 and was used for Wellington repair and overhaul work.

Shrewsbury

Berkshire Aviation Tours converted a DH9 to DH9C configuration for civil use at Monkmoor Aerodrome in 1923.

During the Second World War, a number of factories in Shrewsbury manufactured major components of the Spitfire, supporting the Castle Bromwich factory and its various outstations.

Blenheim IV V5382 was built by Rootes Securities Ltd. (Ken Ellis collection)

Staffordshire

Blythe Bridge

The factory at Blythe Bridge had its origins during the Second World War as a proposed Civilian Repair Depot. Whilst this was never established, it led to the erection of a factory on the site (initially intended for use by Handley Page Ltd, or A.V. Roe & Co. Ltd). In the event, this factory was taken over by **Rootes Securities Ltd** as a shadow factory, building the Blenheim and the Beaufighter (260 aircraft from KV896, made up of 150 Beaufighter VIF, and 110 T.F.X). This factory supplemented production of the Blenheim at Speke, where some 1,070 Handley Page Halifax were also built. Barry Abraham and Phil Butler, writing in *Air Britain Aeromilitaria* Vol.30 Nos. 118, 119 indicate the following production totals: Blenheim I 250 at Speke; Blenheim IV 2,230 mainly at Speke with a few aircraft assembled and tested at either Shawbury (No.9 factory) or Blythe Bridge (No.10 factory)/Meir (No.8 factory). Blenheim V total 942 – two prototypes and fifty production at Speke, the remainder (890 aircraft) at Blythe Bridge. Rootes also prepared for service a total of more than 2,000 Mustang and Harvard aircraft at Blythe Bridge. Creda Cannon now occupies the huge factory at Blythe Bridge.

Burton-on-Trent

The **Civilian Aircraft Co.** was established at 27 Moor Street (the premises of A.S. Briggs & Co.), in 1927 to build the Civilian Coupé. The company was re-registered as the **Civilian Aircraft Co. Ltd** on 3 July 1930 (capital £25,000) at Horninglow Road North. The Coupé

Avro 500 photographed at the Bass's Meadow flying meeting in early August 1913. The aircraft was flown by test pilot F.P. Raynham, with great success. (Alec Brew)

was designed by Harold Boultbee, previously of Handley Page Ltd, and the ABC Hornet-powered prototype G-AAIL flew in July 1929 at Bass's Meadow, Burton-on-Trent.

Bass's Meadow is a strip of land between two arms of the River Trent, the name deriving from the prominent local brewery. It was used for two flying meetings in 1910 and 1913. When used by Sir Alan Cobham for his Aviation Day display in 1933, the site was described as Shobnall Road, Airport Site.

The Civilian Coupé was a high-wing monoplane with folding wings. Initially flown with an ABC Hornet of 85hp, production aircraft used the 100hp Genet Major radial. The cockpit provided seating for two in a slightly staggered side-by-side configuration (like the later Tipsy B) 'to give sociable seating without excessive width'. The change to the Genet Major was probably made due to vibration problems initially experienced with the ABC Hornet. Production took place at Hedon (Hull), the company moving there in February 1931. Five or six aircraft were built before the company closed in 1933.

Navarro Aircraft Syndicate, later **Navarro Aircraft Co. Ltd**: In September 1916, this company was advertising 'No order too small, no order too large. 8 years experience in designing, constructing and experimenting'. In October 1916 the company had offices at 10 Essex Street, Strand, London. In December of the same year, the advertising slogan was 'Aircraft Constructors and Designers'. Although specific products are not known, the company still existed as the **Navarro Aviation Co. Ltd** after the end of the First World War, advertising in 1919 'All British biplanes and triplanes (with metal wings)'. In its guise as Navarro Aviation Co. Ltd, the company operated three Avro 504K for joy-riding.

J.G. Navarro set up **Burton Aircraft & Manufacturing Co.** in July 1917 at Park Street, Burton-on-Trent. The company was advertising 'For main planes and tail units' in August 1918.

See also the entry for Heston (in *British Built Aircraft: Volume 1*) in respect of **Navarro Safety Aircraft Ltd**.

NAVARRO
AIRCRAFT COMP., LTD.

AERONAUTICAL
ENGINEERS

AIRCRAFT CONSTRUCTORS
AND DESIGNERS.

*Materials, Workmanship
and Service guaranteed.*

Up-to-date Machinery of
every description for
wood and metal parts, etc.

ENQUIRES INVITED.

WORKS:
BURTON-ON-TRENT.

'Phone: 554 Burton.   Telegrams: "Navarro, Burton."

A.H.&CO.

*A 1916 advertisement
for Navarro Aircraft
Co. Ltd.*

NAVARRO ALL=BRITISH
BIPLANES & TRIPLANES
(WITH METAL WINGS.)

TWELVE MODELS: FROM 35 H.P. SINGLE SEATER
TO 800 H.P. THIRTY SEATER. £425 TO £8,500.
AEROPLANES FOR SPORTING, TOURING,
COMMERCIAL, MILITARY, AND COLONIAL WORK.

THE NAVARRO AVIATION COMPANY, LTD.,
BURTON-ON-TRENT, ENGLAND.

*A 1919 advertisement
for the Navarro
Aviation Co. Ltd.*

SEND US YOUR
ENQUIRIES FOR
WOODWORK, METAL WORK, PRESSINGS,
TUBEWORK AND WELDING.

BURTON AIRCRAFT and
MANUFACTURING Co., Ltd.,
PARK STREET, BURTON-ON-TRENT.

'Phone: 554 Burton-on-Trent.
Telegrams: "Planes," Burton-on-Trent.

*A 1920 advertisement for
Burton Aircraft &
Manufacturing
Co. Ltd.*

The slow and unpretentious Clutton Tabenor FRED has proved to be a popular design for home-builders.
(Author)

Meir (Stoke-on-Trent)

Meir airfield was the Municipal Airport for Stoke-on-Trent and was opened in May 1934. Airport buildings and hangars from the Elementary Flight Training School were later used by the Staffordshire Potteries factory, sited next to the A50.

Clutton-Tabenor FRED (**F**lying **R**unabout **E**xperimental **D**esign): The FRED is a basic parasol monoplane with a characteristic short-span wing of thick section and high camber, which is designed for home-building. G-ASZY, the first prototype, was designed by Mr E. Clutton and Mr E. Sherry, and was flown on 3 November 1963. This machine was successively powered by a 27hp Triumph motorcycle engine, a Scott A28 and a Lawrance radial engine. In its final form, as the Clutton-Tabenor FRED Series 2, power is provided by a 1,500cc VW engine. The type is now a very popular design, large numbers of which are flying. More than thirty-five aircraft were registered in the UK by the late 1980s.

Rootes Securities Ltd: The Rootes Securities Ltd No.8 factory at Meir assembled Blenheim aircraft from components buit at Speke, prior to the establishment of the No.10 factory at Blythe Bridge, which manufactured complete aircraft. Meir airfield was used for the flight test of aircraft built at the Blythe Bridge shadow factory, which lay just to the south of the airfield and was connected to it by a taxiway. See Blythe Bridge for additional detail.

Perton

Boulton Paul Aircraft Ltd and **Helliwells Ltd** both used the hard runway at RAF Perton for testing aircraft (mainly Douglas Boston/Havoc) when their own grass runways (at Pendeford and Walsall, respectively) were unsuitable.

Seighford Airfield (near Stafford)

Seighford became operational as an RAF airfield at the beginning of 1943, and was re-opened for Boulton Paul use in 1956.

Boulton Paul Aircraft Ltd (see also Wolverhampton and Norwich): Work at Seighford included nine Canberra T.11 conversions, the first of which flew on 29 March 1958. The T.11 was a trainer for the operators of all-weather fighter radar and was fitted with an AI. Mk 17 radar in a conical radome. Significant Canberra modification work was carried out at Seighford up to 1965, including the following examples:

- WT329 modified from Canberra B(I). Mk 8 to become the prototype B.12 for the RNZAF.
- B(I). Mk 8, WT327, was modified for testing the Ferranti AI. Mk 23 radar equipment for the Lightning.
- WV787 was modified for trials of the Buccaneer 'Blue Parrot' radar.

A number of Canberra aircraft were modified for the carriage of AS.30 missiles (one example being Canberra B.15 WH967).

Other activities included flight trials of the Boulton Paul P.111; Javelin trials; conversions of Lightning fighters from F.1 to F.3; and development of electrically signalled controls for the Tay Viscount, VX217. This aircraft flew in 1957 with the world's first electrically signalled

The Boulton Paul P.111A was one of a number of experimental delta wing aircraft flown in the 1950s. VT935 made its first flight at Boscombe Down and is now preserved at Baginton. (J.S. Smith)

Types that were worked on at Seighford included, in particular, the Canberra and Lightning. This is the P.1B prototype fitted with an F.6 underbelly tank mock-up designed by Boulton Paul Aircraft Ltd. (Alec Brew)

Boulton Paul's test airfield at Seighford has become well camouflaged in the agricultural landscape.
(Author)

flight control system. Early work on radar absorbent materials was carried out using Balliol and Canberra aircraft, including Canberra WX161. This diverse activity justified the company's advertising copy: 'Boulton Paul Aircraft Ltd. High performance service aircraft. High-speed research aircraft. Power controls. Electro-hydraulic gun turrets and mountings.'

The cancellation of the TSR.2 caused the British Aircraft Corporation to concentrate its work at Warton, to maintain employment among its experienced workforce. A direct result was the closure of the Hunting Percival factory at Luton. An indirect result was the cessation of Boulton Paul's aircraft manufacturing and test-flying activity, Canberra and Lightning modifications being immediately brought back in-house to Warton, ending Boulton Paul's role in airframe design and manufacture.

Seighford today provides a beautiful rural setting for the activities of the well sign-posted Staffordshire Gliding Club. Many buildings survive, with the large hangars being used for storage by Universal Abrasives. The airfield itself, when seen from the air, is extremely well camouflaged as a result of farming activity.

Stoke-on-Trent

Clutton-Tabenor used the business address of 92 Newlands Street, Shelton, Stoke-on-Trent for marketing the FRED (Flying Runabout Experimental Design) parasol home-built monoplane. The prototype FRED, G-ASZY, first flew on 3 November 1963 at Meir, which see for further details.

Suffolk

Beccles (west of Lowestoft)

The **Sanders Aeroplane Co.**, with works and flying ground at The Common, Beccles, advertised in 1909–11 that its products were 'Designed for rough weather, rough usage and rough landing'. Flying was carried out at Benacre Down, Beccles (also reported as Benacre Denes). The company built at least two types to the design of Capt. H.A. Sanders, who formed the London Aeroplane & Navigation Co. at 23 Blenheim Park Road, Croydon, to publicise his efforts.

The Sanders Type 1 was first flown in October 1909, being destroyed by collision with a telegraph pole on 13 February 1910. The Type 1 was rebuilt in considerably revised form as the Sanders Type 2. In its revised form, it was reminiscent of the Short Type 3, with a biplane foreplane carried on upswept skids. It could also be characterised as being like a biplane version of the Aeronautical Syndicate Valkyrie. The aircraft looked very practical for its day, and was shown at the 1911 Olympia Aero Show. It is not clear how much flying was achieved by this design, although in *British Aircraft Before the Great War* it is reported that three flights were made at Beccles on 30 April 1911. By 1913, it was reported that the company 'appears to have ceased to exist'.

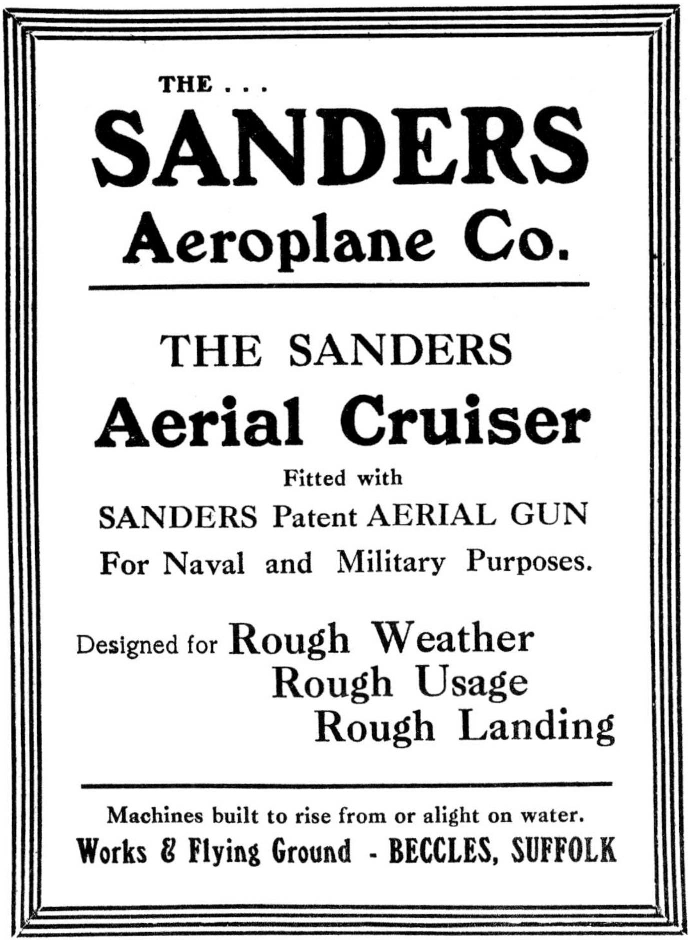

An advertisement for the Sanders Aerial Cruiser, 'Designed for rough weather, rough usage and rough landings'.

THE ...

SANDERS
Aeroplane Co.

THE SANDERS
Aerial Cruiser
Fitted with
SANDERS Patent AERIAL GUN
For Naval and Military Purposes.

Designed for **Rough Weather
Rough Usage
Rough Landing**

Machines built to rise from or alight on water.
Works & Flying Ground - BECCLES, SUFFOLK

Felixstowe

The Royal Naval Air Service station at Felixstowe was the site of a Seaplane Experimental Station during the First World War. In 1917, the facilities at Felixstowe included no less than three seaplane sheds, each measuring 300ft by 200ft and equipped with its own wooden launching slipway. During 1917, forty flying boats were assembled, fitted out and tested at Felixstowe (see the classic book on the subject of the use of the flying boat for anti-submarine patrols in the First World War: *The Spider Web*, Sqn. Ldr. Hallam).

RNAS Felixstowe was commanded by J.C. Porte, who originated many improvements in flying boat design, his particular contribution being improvements in hull shape to improve seaworthiness. Starting with the Curtiss H4 Small America, he developed the Felixstowe F.1 with a new planing hull of greater strength and improved seaworthiness. Fifty American-built Curtiss H4 were erected at Felixstowe, many of them also being re-engined in the process.

The Felixstowe F.1 hull form was migrated to the Curtiss H12 Large America to produce the outstandingly successful Felixstowe F.2A. This type was extensively used in the 'Spider's Web' anti-submarine patrols in the North Sea, covering a 4,000 square mile area centred on the North Hinder light. With a pre-planned search pattern, four F.2A could search this area in three hours. The subsequent Felixstowe F.3 and F.5 designs represented progressive development of the F.2A. More than 600 Felixstowe-designed aircraft were built, including the F.2, F.2A, F.3, F.5, Porte Baby and Felixstowe Fury. The Felixstowe boats were widely contracted to firms including AIRCO; Dick, Kerr & Co. Ltd; Gosport Aircraft Co. Ltd; May, Harden & May; The Norman Thompson Flight Co.; Short Brothers (Rochester & Bedford) Ltd; and S.E. Saunders Ltd. Twenty-three Felixstowe F.3 were constructed by the naval dockyard in Malta.

The **Porte** F.1 Baby was used in experiments carrying a Bristol Scout (No.3028) above the upper centre section in trials which began on 17 May 1916, the fighter being successfully released at a height of 1,000ft. The hull of the Porte Baby was subsequently used to provide

The series of flying boats developed for anti-submarine use at Felixstowe were produced under contract by many firms across the industry. This is a Felixstowe F.3 built by Short Bros at Rochester. (Bombardier Aerospace Belfast)

WRNS accommodation before being used for many years as a hut at Eastward Ho golf course in Felixstowe. The imposing Porte Super Baby triplane (also known as the Felixstowe Fury) N123 was powered by five Rolls-Royce Eagle 8 engines and had a wingspan of 123ft, and a height of 27ft 6ins.

Despite their Felixstowe-designed improvements, these aircraft had a short life in their harsh operating environment. It was the norm for individual aircraft to retire to training duties after only some forty operational missions. Thus aircraft 8661 (*Old '61*) was launched in March 1917, and required its worn-out hull to be replaced, before being retired and dismantled in January 1918 with a total flying life of 368 hours.

Wg Cdr (RNAS) J.C. Porte was accused, in a summons heard at Bow Street Police Court from August 1917, of arranging for secret commissions to be paid to himself on Curtiss machines sold to the Government, and of corruptly receiving large sums as a result. Porte became ill with chronic pulmonary tuberculosis during the hearings, which continued into November. Porte's agent, Casson, pleaded guilty to twelve counts of passing money to Porte, but Porte himself was adjudged to have acted imprudently, but essentially in good faith. The Admiralty valued Porte's services, and the prosecution was withdrawn, such money as had been paid being passed to the Government. Porte joined the Gosport Aircraft Co. in 1919, but died on 22 October 1919 at the early age of thirty-five.

The Seaplane Experimental Station became the **Marine Aircraft Experimental Establishment** from 1 April 1924, moving to Helensburgh upon the outbreak of the Second World War. The MAEE returned to Felixstowe in May 1945. The container port now occupies the site of RNAS Felixstowe.

A number of aircraft made their first flights at the MAEE, or were flown at the MAEE in seaplane form. A sample listing is provided below:

- The Gloster II for the 1924 Schneider Trophy competition (J7504) was flown at Felixstowe on 19 September 1924, but crashed on its first flight.
- The two Gloster III seaplanes (N194, N195) were tested at Felixstowe in August 1925. N194 was flown for the first time on 29 August 1925 and subsequently was placed second in the 1925 Schneider Trophy contest to the American Curtiss R3C-2.
- The Short Crusader N226 (1927 Schneider contender) first flew at Felixstowe on 4 May 1927.
- Hawker types that were tested at Felixstowe in floatplane configuration included Hart J9052 in 1931; Nimrod S1578 in 1932; Osprey S1678; Swedish Hart 1303 in 1934; single-float Osprey S1700 in 1935; and the second Yugoslav Audax in September 1937.

Numerous other types of floatplane and flying boat were tested at Felixstowe.

Ipswich

R.J. Everett Engineering of Sproughton, Ipswich, manufactured a light autogyro, the first of which flew in 1984. The Everett Gyroplane bears a strong resemblance to the Campbell Cricket, with a refined cockpit fairing and large windscreen. A number of the type are flying, and Dick Everett had three on show at the 1996 Cranfield PFA Rally. Flying examples include G-BMZS (Srs 1), G-BOVC (Srs 1) and G-OFRB (Srs 2).

Ransomes, Sims & Jeffries Ltd of Orwell Works, Ipswich, built a large number of aircraft, including the FE2B/C/D/H (more than 350 aircraft), and the AIRCO DH6 (250 aircraft from an order for 400). 100 Vickers Vimy were also ordered but subsequently cancelled. The factory was constructed by Boulton & Paul Ltd, who then passed the jigs and tools over to Ransomes, Sims & Jeffries for FE2 production, enabling Boulton & Paul Ltd to commence

Right: *The Everett Gyroplane resembles the Campbell Cricket and has proven to be one of the more successful types of British sporting autogyro.* (Author)

Below: *Ransomes, Sims & Jeffries Ltd of Ipswich built FE2B B452. The company manufactured some 600 aircraft under contract during the First World War.* (Terry C. Treadwell and Alan C. Wood)

production of the Sopwith Camel. Ransomes, Sims & Jeffries also built the ABC Dragonfly engine.

Described in *The Aeroplane* in February 1936 as 'one of the biggest makers of agricultural implements in the country', the company still exists as Ransomes Ltd, making agricultural/horticultural machinery.

Tibbenham's Aviation Co., of Portland Road, Ipswich, are listed as an aeroplane manufacturer with propeller branch in *The Aviation Pocket-Book of 1919-20*. Nothing else is known.

Leiston

CFM Metal-Fax Ltd (and successors) of Eastlands Industrial Estate, Leiston built the Shadow and Streak Shadow. David Cook designed the CFM (Cook Flying Machines) Shadow and more than 400 of these aircraft have been built in a number of variants. The Shadow and Streak Shadow have been sold in more than thirty-six countries, and have completed many

G-MYDE shows the distinctive configuration of the very successful CFM Shadow. (Author)

notable flights, including from England to Australia in 1987 and 1988. The first prototype Shadow first flew in 1983. Changes in engine from 53hp EC44 Robin to 40hp Rotax 447 and then 50hp Rotax 503 resulted in the Shadow B and C variants.

In 1988, the Streak Shadow was introduced with a 64hp Rotax 532 engine, together with a reduction of wingspan from 33ft to 28ft. The Streak Shadow is a full 'Class A' light aeroplane and claims a 121mph maximum speed; cruise at 75mph at 2.1 gallons per hour; climb to 10,000ft in 8 minutes 36 seconds – all on 64hp. The aircraft has also been flown to 27,000ft altitude. Additional variants include the Star Streak (Rotax 618) and the Super Shadow. In May 1996 the Shadow was being advertised with the slogan: 'Unequalled 100% safety record, 400 Flying Examples'.

In 1995 CFM produced and flew a tailless low-wing design, the CFM Image G-BTUD. Flight testing revealed that delicate handling of the controls was required due to high-pitch sensitivity. David Cook (reported in *Popular Flying*) stated that the design would not be put into production until conventional pilots could fly it without needing unconventional skills.

As with so many British aircraft manufacturers there have been trading difficulties along the way. CFM Metal Fax Ltd went into liquidation in November 1996 and was taken over by CFM Aircraft Ltd in 1997. CFM Aircraft Ltd was, itself, in receivership in autumn 2002, before being taken over by CFM Airborne Inc. of Texas who announced in November 2002 the setting-up of a UK facility, CFM Airborne (UK) Ltd.

Richard Garrett & Sons constructed sixty Royal Aircraft Factory FE2B and 250 FE2B/D nacelles, these being supplied to Boulton & Paul Ltd.

Martlesham Heath (near Ipswich)

Martlesham Heath was the site of the Aeroplane & Armament Experimental Establishment at which civil and military prototypes underwent official testing up to the outbreak of the Second World War. Martlesham Heath took over responsibility for testing military prototypes from the Central Flying School in January 1917. The name of the establishment changed successively from the Aeroplane Testing Squadron, to the Aeroplane Experimental Station, the Aeroplane Experimental Establishment (Home) in April 1920, finally becoming the

Aeroplane & Armament Experimental Establishment on 20 March 1924. From December 1928, all civil aircraft were required to be officially tested at Martlesham Heath prior to the issue of a Certificate of Airworthiness.

Although no manufacturers were based at Martlesham, every new design of the period was flown here. A limited number of aircraft also made their first flight here. These include the **Beardmore** Inflexible J7557 on 5 March 1928, having been transported by ship from Dalmuir; and the first of five **Short** Springbok, J6974, on 19 April 1923. Despite its size and ponderous appearance, the Beardmore Inflexible proved to be very docile and could take off with a run of only 338 yards at maximum weight. Three DH14 Okapi were retained at Martlesham for the endurance testing of the Rolls-Royce Condor engine. The prototype Handley Page Hinaidi J7745 was flown at Martlesham Heath on 26 March 1927.

The Establishment was moved to Boscombe Down immediately on the outbreak of the Second World War, becoming operational there on 20 September 1939. After the Second World War, Martlesham Heath continued to be used for various trials flying as the Armament & Instrument Experimental Unit, this unit being resident until the station closed in 1957. Non-standard aircraft involved in these trials included Avon Lincoln RA716.

Milden (Suffolk) and Earls Colne (Essex)

AJD Engineering of Moat Farm, Milden, Suffolk is run by Tony Ditheridge, whose initials give the company their name. AJD Engineering has links to **Hawker Restorations** of Earls Colne, Essex, and to **Euroair Technical Services** (ETS). These companies have constructed a number of very high-quality replicas of First World War aeroplanes (some of which are fully airworthy), and have repaired, restored and maintain a number of other historic aircraft. Earls Colne is used as the test airfield, aircraft being restored at Milden.

Examples of early aircraft replicas include a Bristol M.1C, Blériot XI, and Avro 504K commissioned by the Chilean Air Force Museum. The Bristol M.1C commemorates the use of this type for the first aerial crossing of the Andes mountain range on 12 December 1918. The replicas for Chile were delivered during February 1990.

Two SE5A replicas were built to the original drawings in early 1991, one for display in the Prince's Mead shopping centre in Farnborough, Hampshire, and the second for the Chilean Air Force Museum. A further SE5A replica was constructed for the RAAF Museum at Point Cook, Victoria, carrying the markings 'A2-31'. In late 1991, an original Avro 504 S-AHAA was under restoration for the Swedish Air Force Museum, and an Avro 504J replica 'C4451' was constructed for the Southampton Hall of Aviation. G-ECXE, an Avro 504K replica, was constructed to the original drawings, with the exception of the engine. G-ECXE 'D8781' made its first flight on 29 September 1994 at Teversham (Cambridge). Avro 504K E3747 was built to flying condition for the RAAF Museum at Point Cook, Victoria.

AJD/ETS were contracted to perform the rebuild of the historic Percival Mew Gull G-AEXF after its accident at Old Warden in July 1991. G-AEXF was flown again on 1 November 1996 following a rebuild that took five and a half years. The year 1992 saw construction of Sopwith Camel G-ASOP/B6291, and Sopwith Pup replica 'A635', which was built in autumn 1992 for export to California. G-ASOP was flown for the first time at Old Warden on 27 July 1993.

Hawker Restorations was founded in 1994 and rebuilt Hurricanes P3351/ZK-TPL and P2902/G-ROBT. In the case of P3351, the company rebuilt the airframe, with engine work to bring the aircraft to flying condition being carried out in New Zealand. Hawker Restorations have been undertaking restoration work on four additional Hurricane aircraft reported to be: G-BRKE/BW853, G-TDTW/5450, G-KAMM/BW881 and G-TWTD/AE977 (Sea Hurricane). AE977 was first flown after restoration at RAF Wattisham in July 2000. Hurricane Z3174 (also quoted as 42025/RCAF5390) is under restoration for static display at the USAF Museum at Dayton, Ohio.

D8781/G-ECKE is an Avro 504K replica built by AJD Engineering and first flown at Cambridge in September 1994. (Author)

A listing of aircraft for which the three companies had been collectively responsible for maintenance, repair and/or overhaul includes: Seafire III G-BUAR/PP972, four Blériot, Sopwith Pup, Mew Gull, BE.2E A1325/G-BVGR, four Avro 504, Bristol M.1C, Spitfire PV202, Bf 109E G-BYDS/1342, Bf 109F-4 10132 and a number of other vintage and combat aircraft. The company also completed the restoration of Spitfire Vc AR614 in late 1999.

Newmarket Heath

Gloster Aircraft Co. Ltd: The prototype Gloster F.9/40 Rampage (later Meteor) DG202/G carried out taxiing trials at Newmarket Heath (then in use as an RAF bomber station) in July 1942. These trials were conducted by Jerry Sayer, and DG202/G was, at that time, fitted with non-flightworthy Rover W.2B engines. This aircraft was subsequently re-engined with Rover W.2B/23 engines and was flown by Michael Daunt at Barford St John on 24 July 1943. This historic prototype, although not the first Meteor to fly, is preserved in the RAF Museum at Cosford.

The first Gloster F.9/40 DG202/G is now preserved at the RAF Museum, Cosford. (Author)

The DH108 Swallow (bottom) was flown for the first time at RAF Woodbridge in May 1946. Three were built, of which this is the second, seen at the 1946 SBAC Show at Radlett. (Handley Page Association)

RAF Woodbridge (north east of Ipswich, Suffolk)

The **de Havilland** DH108 Swallow (TG283) first flew here on 15 May 1946. The type was the first British aircraft to fly faster than the speed of sound, achieving this on 9 September 1948. All three DH108 aircraft were lost in tragic accidents, two of these involving the in-flight break-up of the aircraft.

Warwickshire

Ansty (north east of Coventry)

The airfield at Ansty has its origins with **Air Service Training Ltd**, prior to its being taken over and a factory constructed for use by Standard Motors Ltd during the Second World War (see below).

Armstrong Siddeley maintained an aero engine research unit at Ansty, with experimental test-flying conducted from Bitteswell, see which for further details.

Standard Motors Ltd: Standard Motors built 750 Oxford and 1,066 Mosquito FB VI aircraft, using Ansty for final assembly, flight test and delivery. Orders for an additional 434 Mosquito FB VI were cancelled. The Ansty site remains in use by Rolls-Royce Ltd.

Baginton

Sir W.G. Armstrong Whitworth Aircraft Ltd, and its successors, used Baginton (Coventry Airport), both as a factory, and as a flight test airfield. Other sites used include Bitteswell (Leicestershire); Parkside, Coventry; and Whitley Abbey, see which for further information.

The major types manufactured by Sir W.G. Armstrong Whitworth Aircraft Ltd at its various sites were as listed below:

Type	Numbers produced and comments
Armstrong Whitworth Siskin III/IIIA	First flown on 7 May 1923. A total of 485 built, more than 250 of which were contracted as follows: The Blackburn Aeroplane & Motor Co. Ltd (42), The Bristol Aeroplane Co. Ltd (85), Gloster Aircraft Co. Ltd (74) and Vickers (Aviation) Ltd (52), thereby spreading familiarity with metal construction techniques across the industry. At least ten Siskin V were built from an order of seventy for Romania.
Armstrong Whitworth Atlas	478 built, 175 as dual-control trainers (some sources state 486, also 446). The first prototype J8675 (previously G-EBLK) was first flown at Whitley on 10 May 1925.
Hawker Hart	456 Hawker Hart and Hart Trainer contract production.

The Siskin was the most important fighter produced by Armstrong Whitworth. J2982 is the second of three pre-production Siskin III and was later registered as G-EBJQ to compete in the 1924 King's Cup Air Race. (Ray Williams archive)

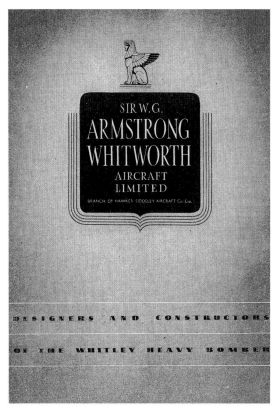

Armstrong Whitworth – the proud
designers of the Whitley bomber.
(BAE SYSTEMS plc)

Armstrong Whitworth were responsible
for night-fighter variants of the Gloster
Meteor. (BAE SYSTEMS plc)

Whitley final assembly underway at Baginton. (Ray Williams)

Type	Numbers produced and comments
Armstrong Whitworth A.W.38 Whitley	1,814 twin–engine monoplane bombers. Prototype K4586 was first flown on 17 March 1936.
Avro Lancaster	A total of 1,329 comprising 919 Mk I, 300 Mk II, 110 Mk III. Some of the Armstrong Whitworth-built Lancaster II aircraft were assembled at Sywell, Northampton. Other dispersed facilities were operated at Leicester and Nuneaton. Some aircraft assembled and flown at Bitteswell.
Avro Lincoln	281 aircraft, all built at Baginton. Some sources state 299, but this discrepancy is believed to arise from eighteen aircraft ordered from Armstrong Whitworth, but diverted to A.V. Roe & Co. Ltd for delivery to Argentina as B-013 to B-030.
Gloster Meteor	Forty-five Meteor F.4; 430 Meteor F.8 (the last aircraft being converted to prone pilot configuration); and more than 610 night fighter Meteor made up as follows – 352 NF.11 for the RAF (plus

Sir W.G. Armstrong Whitworth Aircraft Ltd constructed 281 Avro Lincoln bombers under contract. (Author)

Type	Numbers produced and comments
Gloster Meteor *continued*	three prototypes and twenty aircraft exported to Denmark), 100 N.F.12 (prototype WS590, flown 21 April 1953), forty N.F.13 (prototype WM308, flown 21 December 1952) and 100 N.F.14 (prototype WM261 (from N.F.12)). The first Meteor N.F.11 WA546 was flown from Baginton on 31 May 1950.
Hawker Sea Hawk	520 Sea Hawk assembled at Bitteswell (all except the first thirty-five aircraft, which were assembled by Hawker Aircraft Ltd at Kingston upon Thames and test-flown at Dunsfold).
Gloster Javelin	133 (marks FAW. 6, 7, 9 at Bitteswell, see which for further details).
Hawker Hunter	278 Hunter (marks as follows: forty-five F.2; 105 F.5; 128 F.6; and four Hunter T.7 and at least fourteen T.8 conversions from F.4).
Armstrong Whitworth Argosy	Eighteen civil (A.W.650) and fifty-six military Argosy (A.W.660). The civil machines ended their active lives with Sagittair/Air Bridge Carriers at Castle Donington, and Midland Air Cargo at Coventry.

Sir W.G. Armstrong Whitworth Aircraft Ltd transferred their activities from Whitley Abbey to Baginton in 1936. The first new type to be flown at Baginton was the A.W.35 Scimitar on 26 May 1936.

Production of Sea Hawk centre sections photographed at Baginton in February 1953. (Ray Williams)

PACEMAKERS OF PROGRESS

Leaders in an age of great development, renowned for
30 years for high performance Civil and Military Aircraft

AWA

SIR W. G. ARMSTRONG WHITWORTH AIRCRAFT LIMITED, BAGINTON, COVENTRY

MEMBER OF THE HAWKER SIDDELEY GROUP

An Armstrong Whitworth advertisement featuring the A.W.52 and the Apollo. In the event, neither was to prove to be a 'Pacemaker of Progress'. (BAE SYSTEMS plc)

Some miscellaneous activities at Baginton are summarised below:

- An experimental laminar flow wing was fitted to Hurricane Z3627 at Baginton, flying in this form on 23 March 1945.
- Baginton was used as a support and maintenance base during the Berlin Air Lift, with many RAF Avro York transport aircraft being overhauled here.
- Two Avro Tudor 3 aircraft were delivered to Baginton in 1948 to be fitted out with suitably luxurious cabin appointments to suit their role as VIP transports for the use of cabinet ministers. Emerging as VP301 and VP312, these aircraft subsequently returned to civil marks as G-AIYA and G-AJKC.

The unsuccessful A.W.55 Apollo airliner, designed to the Brabazon Type II specification, was built at Baginton, the prototype VX220 (later G-AIYN) flying on 10 April 1949. The second aircraft VX224/G-AMCH, first flew on 12 December 1952 and was operated for less than thirty hours before being consigned to structural testing at Farnborough.

The prone pilot Meteor conversion WK935 (the last of the Armstrong Whitworth batch of F. Mk 8 aircraft) was the last Armstrong Whitworth-built aircraft to make its first flight from Baginton, on 10 February 1954. The Baginton factory was closed in July 1965 following the cancellation of the HS.681 V/STOL transport aircraft.

The area has now been developed into the Middlemarch Industrial Park, its Armstrong Whitworth connections being neatly recalled by the name of the entrance road: Siskin Parkway. In summer 1997 only a few original buildings remained, these being in the process of being demolished.

Flight testing of **Armstrong Siddeley Motors Ltd** piston engines was conducted at Baginton, prior to the opening of Bitteswell. Engines tested included the Armstrong Siddeley Tiger and Deerhound. Whitley II K7243 was used for testing of the Armstrong Siddeley Deerhound and was flown for the first time with this engine at Baginton in January 1935. Another Armstrong Siddeley test aircraft was the sole Hawker Hoopoe N237. Originally flown at Brooklands with a Bristol Mercury II, the Hoopoe went on to fly with the Armstrong Siddeley Jaguar V, and the Panther II and III.

The **Dunlop Ltd** flight test fleet was based at Baginton during the Second World War, with, among other aircraft, Wellington BK187. Dunlop testing moved to Honiley in 1944 to take advantage of its hard runway.

Metropolitan-Vickers Electrical Co. Ltd was involved in the development of early jet engines, engine flight-testing being carried out at Baginton and Bitteswell. The Metropolitan-Vickers F.2/1 was first flown at Baginton in the tail of Lancaster BT308 (the Lancaster prototype) on 29 June 1943. Lancaster LL735 was also flown with a tail-mounted Metropolitan-Vickers F.2/1. The Metropolitan-Vickers Beryl was flown in Meteor 4 RA490. For further details of Armstrong Siddeley and Metropolitan-Vickers engine testing, see Bitteswell.

Bidford Gliding site (north east of Evesham)

The AMF Chevvron prototype made it first flight at Bidford during 1983. For further details, see the entry for Hungerford and Membury in *British Built Aircraft: Volume 3*.

Billesley (near Stratford upon Avon)

In May 1915, the **D&W** racing monoplane was being tested at Billesley, flown by Mr Summerfield of Melton Mowbray. Described as a diminutive monoplane, it was nevertheless said to be coping well with a field whose surface was full of ridges. Nothing else is known.

In April 1916, the **Midland School of Flying** were reported as having a fuselage tractor biplane nearly finished, powered by a 60hp Anzani. The company used Blériot aircraft initially, but had six Caudron biplanes under construction at the firm's works at King's Heath. The Flying Ground, known as Billesley Aerodrome, King's Heath, had been cleared of trees and other obstructions and new hangars were being erected.

RAF Edgehill

The **Gloster Aircraft Co. Ltd** used the airfield at Edgehill for testing of the E.28/39 in 1942 and 1943, exploiting the long runway available.

Honiley (south west of Coventry)

Burgoyne-Stirling Dicer: This single-seat low-wing monoplane was built in 1939, but not flown until 31 March 1946. Don Burgoyne of Knowle dabbled with a range of light and ultra-light aircraft pre- and post-war. The Dicer has somewhat uncertain origins, having been built by Mr Burgoyne and taken over post-war by Mr H. Stirling. It carried the marks G-AECN, but was never legally registered as such, these marks having been allocated to a Flying Flea previously built by Mr Burgoyne. In appearance, the aircraft resembled a Dart Kitten, with a markedly longer, glider-like fuselage (rather like the rear fuselage of a Kirby Cadet). One source suggests that components were obtained from a number of other aircraft, including

Kronfeld (BAC) Drone parts, BA Swallow outer wings, together with the engine from an American-built Aeronca E.113C (also reported as being the engine of Dart Pup G-AELR). The Dicer also flew from RAF Wymeswold and Burton-on-the-Wolds. Mr Burgoyne at various times also owned the unregistered Taylor C.103, a Klemm L26, a BA Swallow, and at least two Drones.

Dunlop Ltd carried out flight-testing at Honiley using Wellington BK187 and Buckingham I KV749. This activity was subsequently transferred to Birmingham Elmdon.

Rugby

Although they were never an aircraft manufacturer, it is worth recording that **The British Thomson-Houston Co.** at Rugby was responsible for the construction of the first Whittle jet engine, which was run successfully in April 1937.

Warwick

Warwick Aviation Co. Ltd, (incorporating Castle Engineering Works), 'Aircraft Constructors, Saltisford, Warwick, England (Office and Works). Air Ministry AID Approval No 964193/38'. This advertisement was in use at the start of 1946, and was illustrated by an artist's impression of an aircraft resembling a retractable undercarriage Moth Minor. Other advertising indicates that the company was a specialist in light alloy construction.

A 1946 advertisement for Warwick Aviation.

By January 1947, the company's aircraft manufacturing ambitions seem to have faded; its name was changed to **Warwick Productions Co. Ltd**, and its advertising material was promoting a range of domestic goods.

West Midlands

The West Midlands comprises the unitary authorities of Birmingham, Coventry, Dudley, Sandwell, Solihull, Walsall and Wolverhampton.

Birmingham

The **Austin Motor Co. Ltd**, of Northfield Works at Longbridge, south west Birmingham, was set up when Herbert Austin left the Wolseley Sheep Shearing Machine Co. The company telegraphic address was 'Speedily', Northfield. Austin was advertising for skilled workers under the style **Austin Motor Co. (1914) Ltd** in January 1914. The aircraft department was initially run by J.D. North on his departure from Grahame-White.

During the First World War, the Austin Motor Co. was engaged in extensive contract production, and also manufactured aircraft of their own design. A works was built specifically for aircraft construction, with an airfield immediately to its south. The main types built by Austin were the SE5A, and the RE8, production numbers being as follows:

- RE7: At least thirty (some sources fifty-two, not all of which are confirmed to have been delivered). A further 100 were cancelled.
- RE8: A total of 300 in three batches of 100, 150 and fifty aircraft (some sources state 250).
- SE5A: 1,550, with a further 250 cancelled.
- Austin Ball A.F.B.1 Scout: One only, serial number B9909 flown July 1917.
- A.F.T.3 Osprey triplane fighter: one built, serial number X15, first flown at Castle Bromwich in February 1918 and tested at Martlesham Heath in March 1918.
- Austin Greyhound: Three built in 1919 powered by the unreliable ABC Dragonfly, the first being H4317 flown in May 1919.
- Bristol F.2B Fighter: Two (possibly four) only from an order of no less than 600.

First World War production also included some 2,500 engines at a peak rate of 350 per month. Immediately after the end of the war, Austin attempted to enter the private aircraft market with the Whippet, and Kestrel, the latter being a side-by-side two-seat biplane, of which only a single example, G-EATR, was built.

The Whippet was very successful as a design, and although only five were built, they were each flown for several years during the 1920s, and two were exported to New Zealand. John Kenworthy, who had worked with de Havilland and Folland at the Royal Aircraft Factory, designed the type. This 21ft 6in span biplane featured folding wings to fit in an 8ft by 18ft garage, and weighed less than 600lb when empty. It was in many ways a Currie Wot built before its time. Sold under the advertising slogan 'The King of Exhilaration', the Whippet was also an early example of steel tube construction. The prototype K-158 flew in mid-1919 and was allocated the registration G-EAGS in December of the same year.

During the Second World War, **Austin Motors Ltd** was again heavily engaged in contract production, building the Fairey Battle (1,029), Short Stirling (620), Avro Lancaster (total 330: 150 Mk I and 180 Mk VII) and Airspeed Horsa (365, some sources state fuselages only). The company also built at least 300 Hurricanes, many of these being then shipped to the USSR. Components equivalent to about 200 additional Hurricane aircraft were also manufactured.

The Austin Motor Co. manufactured aircraft under contract in both world wars. First World War production concentrated on the SE5A and RE8. This Austin-built RE8 is in service with No.52 Squadron RFC. (Terry C. Treadwell and Alan C. Wood)

H6058 is a Siddeley Puma-powered Bristol F.2B Fighter built by Austin Motors Ltd. (Austin Motors Ltd via Ken Ellis)

The *Austin*

"WHIPPET"

The PLANE for the OWNER-PILOT.

The age of practical private aviation is here. Everyone who has a desire to possess and fly his own plane can now do'so without entailing fabulous expense.

Approximately £500, or less than the cost of a good car, will buy the Austin Whippet, a single-seater biplane of small dimensions but great capabilities.

The Austin Whippet can be housed in an ordinary garage when its wings are folded, and can be handled with ease by anyone.

Wonderfully stable in flight, it will climb to 10,000 feet and attain a speed of 85 miles per hour. Of steel construction throughout, it is built essentially for safety.

THE AUSTIN MOTOR CO., LTD.

Head Office - : Northfield, Birmingham.
Telephone : King's Norton 230   Telegrams : "Speedily, Northfield."

LONDON - - - - 479-483, Oxford Street, W. 1.
MANCHESTER - - - - - 130, Deansgate.
And at PARIS and BRUSSELS.

A January 1920 advertisement for the Austin Whippet. The type was also promoted with the slogan, 'The King of Exhilaration'.

HM King George VI and Queen Elizabeth inspect the Fairey Battle production facilities of Austin Motors Ltd at Longbridge. (BL Cars via Geoff Negus)

Research by Barry Abraham indicates that Horsa production was carried out at Longbridge West Works, separate from the Cofton Hackett Works. He also indicates that three contracts were let for 100, then 200 Mk I, followed by sixty-five aircraft from a contract for eighty-nine Horsa Mk II. The type was also built by Harris Lebus of Tottenham, and by a large industrial group which was managed by a committee that was, in turn, chaired by Harris Lebus. During the Second World War, Austin Motors also built 795 Horsa centre-fuselages as part of the Group activity managed by Harris Lebus.

The twenty-three-acre Longbridge aircraft works were among the largest in the 'shadow' factory scheme, and included substantial engine assembly and test facilities. The factory was initially tasked, with others in the shadow production scheme, with manufacturing Bristol Mercury engine components. The scheme was subsequently modified to encompass production of complete engines, and aircraft.

The company airfield, known as Cofton Hackett, was circular with a maximum run of only 400 yards, and was immediately adjacent to the works, but forty feet below it. Consequently, completed aircraft had to be transported down to airfield level using a specially constructed lift before they could be flown. The first Austin-built Battle L4935 was flown during July 1938. Following production of the Battle, the Longbridge Factory transferred to Hurricane repair, and then (1940) to the manufacture of complete Hurricane aircraft.

A new factory was built at Marston Green, close to Elmdon (Birmingham Airport), and this was then used for the construction of first Stirling and then Lancaster bombers. The aircraft were towed onto the airfield across a bridge over the railway line that separated the factory from the airfield.

A Handley Page O/400 built by The Birmingham & Midland Carriage Co. towers over the first Austin Whippet K.158. (Austin Motors Ltd via Ken Ellis)

Second World War production by Austin Motors Ltd totalled more than 2,400 aircraft, and many engines including 14,300 complete Mercury and Pegasus, 42,185 sets of engine parts for Mercury and Pegasus, 23,000 sets of engine parts for the Merlin, and components for other aircraft including wing and centre sections for 1,100 Master and 3,000 Beaufighter aircraft.

Birmingham & Midland Carriage Co.: Contract production by this firm during the First World War comprised the DH10 and Handley Page O/400. 100 DH10 were ordered, but the number completed is not known with certainty, although it may have been as many as sixty. One hundred and four Handley Page O/400 were ordered in three batches, the first aircraft being D5401. These aircraft were built at Middlemore Lane, Handsworth and flown from an airfield on the west side of Halford's Lane, Smethwick, opposite the West Bromwich Albion football ground.

During the Second World War, the **Birmingham Railway Carriage & Wagon Co. Ltd** built the General Aircraft Hamilcar X, and participated in group-production of the Hamilcar glider, in association with the CWS and AC Motors Ltd. The company also manufactured the chassis and other components for the Cromwell tank.

The **Metropolitan Carriage, Wagon & Finance Co.**: Sub-contract production by this firm during the First World War comprised 100 Handley Page O/400, the first aircraft being D4561. The company was also contracted for 200 Vimy, which were subsequently cancelled. The company was a subsidiary of Vickers Ltd, being based alongside Wolseley at Adderley Park and was also known as the Metropolitan Railway Carriage & Wagon Co. Its factory was subsequently taken over by Wolseley Motors Ltd as that firm expanded.

Note that the similarity of company names between the Birmingham & Midland Carriage Co., Birmingham Railway Carriage & Wagon Co., Metropolitan Carriage Wagon & Finance

Co. and the Metropolitan Railway, Carriage & Wagon Co. make it possible that these organ-isations were linked, or even the same company variously cited in different publications.

Carr's Paper Mill, Shirley, Birmingham worked under sub-contract to Austin Motors Ltd on the production of components including bomb-bay doors and wing trailing edges for the Short Stirling.

Dunlop Ltd flight-testing was carried out at Elmdon (Birmingham Airport), following on from Honiley. The fleet included Lancaster PB752, Wellington BK563, Wellington BK563, Avro Lincoln RE253 and an Albemarle IV. For other aircraft operated, see Honiley and Baginton. The test-fleet had been disbanded by 1949.

Joseph Evans & Sons Ltd, of Liverpool Street, Birmingham, is listed in *The Aviation Pocket-Book 1919-20* as an aircraft manufacturer, and advertised that they 'specialise in component parts for Short, BE, FE, RE and Farman designs'.

Harris & Sheldon Ltd, of Stafford Street, Birmingham: Contract production during the First World War comprised 100 Bristol Fighter aircraft, the first aircraft having the serial F5074. Harris & Sheldon initially advertised 'Metal Parts for Aeroplanes', followed in November 1916 by – 'Makers of every description of metal parts for aeroplanes – petrol tanks, petrol cocks, sockets, plates, levers, windscreens...'. By May 1917 the company was describing itself as 'Manufacturers of component parts for aeroplanes in metal and wood. Contractors to Admiralty and War Office'.

Later advertising in November 1917 mentioned 'Wood Parts: hollow spars and struts, wings, tail booms, rudders, elevators, complete gunner's seats; Metal Parts: pressed parts, petrol tanks, Levers, sheet metal work, wiring plates, wind screens, oxyacetylene welding. Aircraft constructors to The War Office'. Telegrams: 'Fittings', Birmingham.

Hoskins & Sewell Ltd, of Bordesley, Birmingham, was advertising in August 1918: 'We are making parts for the DH Machines for immediate delivery'.

During the Second World War, some 1,800 sets of Horsa glider wings were built as part of a production group including **LMS, LNER** and the **Craven Carriage Works.**

Lucas (now Lucas Industries plc), Great King Street, Birmingham: in addition to their well-known magneto manufacturing activities, Lucas were sub-contracted to build Fairey Battle components, and manufactured no less than 12,500 Spitfire wing sub-assemblies. Some of this work was dispersed to the Cadbury factory at Bournville. Other manufacture by Lucas

A May 1917 advertisement for aeroplane parts manufactured by Harris & Sheldon Ltd.

included Boulton Paul gun turrets for a number of types, these being manufactured at Sparkhill.

Motor engineer A.P. Maxfield, of 171 Highfield Road, Saltley, built the **Maxfield** 1909 monoplane. The aircraft was single engined, but featured twin propellers. The type was flown successfully at Castle Bromwich in September/October 1909 (see also the entry for Castle Bromwich).

The Rover Company Ltd: Rover was much involved in engine manufacture during the Second World War. The No.1 Shadow Factory at Acocks Green was used for engine production from July 1937. This factory initially manufactured Bristol Hercules engines and was later a key contributor to gas turbine development and manufacture, before this responsibility was handed to Rolls-Royce in 1943. Acocks Green was also used for the manufacture of Stirling components. The No.2 Shadow Factory at Solihull (the present Land Rover plant) is believed to have participated in both airframe (Stirling components) and aero engine production. Cheetah engines were made by Rover at Tyseley, Birmingham, and also in Coventry.

Mr Fred Taylor built a series of very light aircraft during the late 1930s. One of these aircraft, the C.103 Wagtail, although never registered or certificated, was a thoroughly workmanlike design. The C.103 was similar to the Luton Minor, but with a rather more complex undercarriage and wing bracing strut arrangement and much larger tail surfaces. This aircraft was flown from Dunton Hall Farm, near Birmingham (also reported as possibly at Marston Green), having, like all his designs, been built at Mr Taylor's home. The type designations ran in sequence: A.101; B.102 (a modification of the A.101); C.103; D.104. None were formally registered and it is not clear which of them were flown – certainly not the D.104, which was intended as a ground-based trainer. The C.103 continued to fly locally (Castle Bromwich, Dunton and Lea Marston) until at least 1948.

The Taylor C.103 Wagtail was one of a series of unofficial (unregistered) home-built aircraft built and flown in the Birmingham area by Mr Fred Taylor. (Ken Ellis collection)

D6856 is a Wolseley-built SE5A preserved at the South African National War Museum in Johannesburg. (Author)

Wolseley Motors Ltd, of Adderley Park, Birmingham, became a subsidiary of Vickers Ltd in 1901, having originally been a manufacturer of sheep-shearing equipment for the Australian market. In 1911, the company style was the **Wolseley Tool & Motor Car Co. Ltd**. (prop. Vickers Ltd). Contract production during the First World War comprised BE2C/D/E/F (240) and SE5A (450, also quoted as 431). An order for 150 Sopwith Salamander was subsequently cancelled. Wolseley advertised as 'Manufacturers of Aviation Motors and Aircraft'.

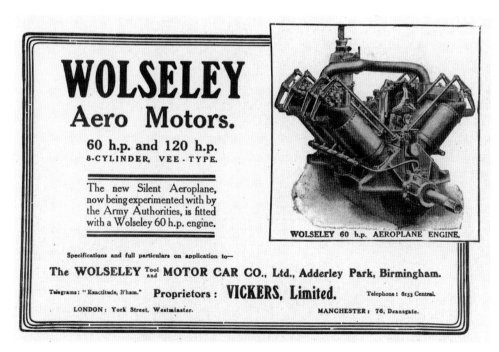

An early advertisement for Wolseley Motors, the company then styling itself The Wolseley Tool and Motor Car Co. Ltd.

In 1913, the twenty-one-acre factory was said to be the largest in Europe solely devoted to manufacture of motor vehicles. During the First World War 4,500 complete engines and the equivalent of 1,500 more as spares were constructed. In addition to some 700 complete aircraft, 850 wings and tail planes, and 6,000 propellers were manufactured. Initial problems with crankshaft failures on Wolseley-built Hispano Suiza engines seriously hampered delivery of SE5A aircraft.

William Morris, later Lord Nuffield, took over Wolseley in 1927 and it became part of Morris Motors Ltd in 1935. From around 1930, operations were concentrated at Drews Lane, Ward End, Birmingham. Lord Nuffield was excluded from the 'shadow' scheme when it started in 1936 (mainly because he wished to manufacture complete engines, rather than components), and withdrew from aero engine manufacture in October 1936.

During the Second World War, Wolseley Motors built 714 sets of Horsa outer wings as part of the group activity managed by Harris Lebus.

Castle Bromwich

Initially, the open space at Castle Bromwich was laid out for use as playing fields, these being used periodically for flying prior to the First World War, under the auspices of the Midland Aero Club. At the outbreak of the First World War, The War Office requisitioned the flying ground. In addition to RFC/RAF operations, this was the site of **No.14 Aircraft Acceptance Park**. By the end of the First World War, the Acceptance Park had thirty storage sheds and hangars.

Brooklands Aviation Ltd repaired a number of Wellington aircraft at Castle Bromwich, and at Sywell, Northamptonshire. Alex Henshaw reports in *Sigh for a Merlin* that the Castle Bromwich flight test department test-flew seventy-one Wellington aircraft at Castle Bromwich that had been repaired by Brooklands Aviation.

The **Maxfield** monoplane of 1909 was built by Alfred Pericles Maxfield and flew successfully from 24 September to 2 October at Castle Bromwich Golf Links, earning Mr Maxfield the title of 'Birmingham's first flying man'. The aircraft, which was his third design, featured front and rear biplane elevators and tail surfaces, and a single engine driving twin propellers.

Sunbeam Motor Car Co. Ltd: The Sunbeam Bomber (Admiralty Type 7) N515 was first flown at castle Bromwich in 1917. It was not successful, and only a single example was built.

Vickers-Armstrongs Ltd: The Spitfire, Seafire and Lancaster were all produced at the Vickers-Armstrongs run shadow factory at Castle Bromwich. The Nuffield Organisation originally built the huge factory (the enormous site covered 345 acres), work on its construction starting on 14 July 1938.

The Nuffield Organisation was an enterprise versed in the disciplines of mass production in the motor industry, headed by Lord Nuffield, previously Sir William Morris and the founder of Morris Motors Ltd. As such, they faced a significant problem, in that the pace of early Spitfire airframe and engine development (and the resultant frequent modification required) was such that the design was inadequately 'frozen', but 'lightly-chilled' at best. This was totally counter to the methods of the motor industry and caused extreme difficulty in the transition to production. An initial order for 1,000 Spitfire was placed on 12 April 1939. The Nuffield Organisation completed a total of nine aircraft, with the first example being delivered on 17 June 1940. The problems that arose in establishing production resulted in the transfer of the Castle Bromwich factory to the control of Vickers-Armstrongs Ltd on 20 May 1940.

Production of Spitfires at Castle Bromwich eventually ran at up to 320 per month and the last Castle Bromwich-built aircraft was test-flown on 30 November 1945. As with the Southern

Supermarine Spitfire LF.XVI TB302 is one of many examples to have been built at the Castle Bromwich shadow factory. (H.E. North)

Final assembly of the Lancaster bomber at Castle Bromwich. The nearest aircraft is HK649. (Richard R. Leader via Geoff Negus)

manufacturing sites, a dispersed production system was used, with many West Midlands towns having a share of the effort. Fuselages were also supplied from the Vickers-Armstrongs factory at South Marston, Wiltshire. The total number of Spitfires built at Castle Bromwich ranges from 11,555 to 11,939, dependent upon the reference source. Alex Henshaw reports that 11,694 Spitfire were built under the control of Castle Bromwich, with production split between Castle Bromwich, Cosford and Desford (the vast majority of these being built at Castle Bromwich). What is indisputable is that Castle Bromwich was responsible for the construction of more Spitfire aircraft than all the other factories combined.

Vickers-Armstrongs Ltd built 300 Lancaster bombers at Castle Bromwich (plus twelve others assembled from parts manufactured elsewhere by A.V. Roe & Co. Ltd). The Lancaster production rate built up to twenty-five aircraft per month in December 1944. Different dates are given for the first flight of the initial Castle Bromwich-built machine, Alex Henshaw states in *Sigh for a Merlin* that DV272 was the aircraft concerned, and that it flew on 16 October 1943. Harry Holmes, in *Avro – The History of an Aircraft Company*, indicates that the first aircraft was completed in November 1943 and the last in August 1945. There is also some doubt over the total number built – various sources quoting figures between 300 and 535! Alex Henshaw states that 305 Lancaster were built at Castle Bromwich.

The airfield suffered from poor visibility due to the smoke of Birmingham and had a balloon barrage on three sides. There were also power station cooling towers less than three miles to the east. Castle Bromwich airfield closed in March 1960, and the site was then developed into the monstrous Castle Vale housing estate.

Wolseley Motors Ltd used three Hawker Tomtit aircraft, G-AASI, G-ABAX, G-ABOD, based at Castle Bromwich from early 1934, in support of development of Wolseley radial engines. G-ABOD was flown with the A.R.2, A.R.7, A.R.9, Aries and Aquarius engines.

Coventry

Aircraft manufacture in Coventry is discussed below in the following sequence: (i) Sir W.G. Armstrong Whitworth Aircraft Ltd, its forebears and successors, followed by (ii) an alphabetical listing of other Coventry-based companies.

The Siddeley-Deasy Motor Car Co. Ltd, Parkside, Coventry: The origin of this company was The Deasy Motor Car Manufacturing Co., which was formed by Captain H.P. Deasy at Parkside in 1906. In 1912, the company was re-named The Siddeley-Deasy Motor Car Co. Ltd. John Siddeley was a champion cyclist (reputed to have been the first man to have cycled from Lands End to John o'Groats), who ran Wolseley before joining up with Capt. Deasy for car manufacture.

Siddeley-Deasy received its first order for aircraft in December 1914. During the First World War the number of employees grew from 400 to 6,000, the factory occupying a twenty-five-acre site. In August 1918, the company was advertising as 'Contractors to HM Air Ministry: Designers and constructors of Aero Engines, Aeroplanes and Luxurious motor carriages'.

The main production type was the RE8 (1,030 built, six of which were completed as RT1), together with the RE7 (100), and DH10 (fifty ordered, twenty-eight completed (some sources state eighteen)).

John Lloyd was Assistant Chief Designer of Siddeley-Deasy from 1917 to 1924, having been the Chief Stress Engineer of the Royal Aircraft Factory from 1914 to 1917. Lloyd was responsible for the SR2 Siskin fighter, and was Chief Designer of Sir W.G. Armstrong Whitworth Aircraft Ltd from 1924 until 1948, becoming Technical Director thereafter. The first Siddeley SR2 Siskin was built 'in a shed' on London Road, Coventry, close to Parkside, in 1918. This machine was later developed into the Armstrong Whitworth Siskin, following

Hawker Tomtit G-ABAX was one of three owned by Wolseley Motors Ltd and fitted with Wolseley A.R. 9 engines for the 1935 King's Cup Air Race. The three Tomtits were based at Castle Bromwich and used for engine trials. (via J.S. Smith)

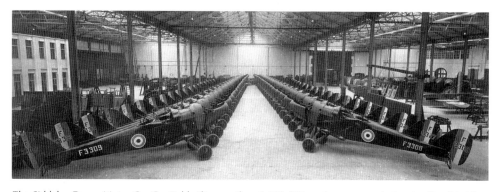

The Siddeley-Deasy Motor Car Co. Ltd built more than 1,000 RE8 under contract during the First World War. (Terry C. Treadwell and Alan C. Wood)

The Siddeley SR2 Siskin C4541 was developed into the Armstrong Whitworth Siskin, of which nearly 400 were built. The production type was characterised by its sesquiplane layout, with the lower wing being of much smaller chord and area than the upper. (Ray Williams archive)

the merger of the Armstrong Whitworth and Siddeley-Deasy companies. The Siddeley-Deasy Motor Car Co. Ltd carried out its development flying at Radford, where the SR2 Siskin C4541 made its first flight in July 1919.

Siddeley-Deasy also built the BHP (Beardmore-Halford-Pullinger) engine, later known as the Siddeley Puma, which was produced at up to 250 per week. Siddeley-Deasy made use of Armstrong Whitworth as subcontractors for Puma production, thus establishing the initial relationship between the two companies.

The Parkside factory closed in 1994 and the site was in the process of being cleared in mid-1997 to create Coventry Science & Technology Park. Radford was at that time an assembly plant for Jaguar XJ6 and V12 engines.

Sir W.G. Armstrong Whitworth Aircraft Ltd: Sir W.G. Armstrong, Whitworth & Co. Ltd of Newcastle and the Siddeley-Deasy Motor Car Co. Ltd of Coventry came together when Armstrong Whitworth purchased the shares of Siddeley-Deasy. As a result, the **Armstrong Siddeley Development Co. Ltd** was formed in 1919 (at London Road, Coventry). Two subsidiaries were subsequently created: **Sir W.G. Armstrong Whitworth Aircraft Ltd** (to build aircraft) and **Armstrong Siddeley Motors Ltd** (to build cars and engines, from October 1919).

In December 1926, John Siddeley purchased all the shares of the **Armstrong Whitworth Development Co. Ltd**, although the aircraft and engine firms continued to trade under their original names.

In May 1928, John Siddeley acquired the shares of **A.V. Roe & Co. Ltd**, this setting the scene for the formation of the **Hawker Siddeley Aircraft Co. Ltd**. In July 1935 Hawker Siddeley Aircraft Co. Ltd took over the whole of **Armstrong Siddeley Development Co.** (comprising **Sir W.G. Armstrong Whitworth Aircraft Ltd**, **A.V. Roe & Co. Ltd**, **Armstrong Siddeley Motors Ltd** and **AST Ltd**), and half the shares of **Hawker Aircraft Ltd**, which already owned Gloster Aircraft Co. Ltd. The individual companies within the group continued to trade under their original names up to the 1960s.

Armstrong Whitworth was merged within the Hawker Siddeley Group with Gloster Aircraft Co. Ltd to form the **Whitworth Gloster Division** in 1961. In 1963, the name of this division was changed to the **Avro Whitworth Division**, before the identities of the founder companies were absorbed into the corporate identity of **Hawker Siddeley Aviation Ltd**, also in 1963. **Armstrong Siddeley Motors Ltd** was merged with **Bristol Aero-Engines Ltd** to form **Bristol Siddeley Engines Ltd** in 1958. Bristol Siddeley was, itself, sold to Rolls-Royce Ltd on 5 October 1966.

The main operating locations of Sir W.G. Armstrong Whitworth Aircraft Ltd were Parkside, Whitley Abbey (West Midlands) Baginton (Warwickshire) and Bitteswell (Leicestershire). In addition to their own designs, the company carried out extensive sub-contract work for other firms within the Hawker Siddeley Group.

Armstrong Whitworth purchased land at Whitley Abbey in 1920 for use as an airfield and factory. Once construction was completed in 1923, the Armstrong Whitworth aircraft works were moved from Parkside to Whitley Abbey. Design activity remained at Parkside until 1930. Armstrong Whitworth transferred their activities from Whitley Abbey to Baginton in 1936.

In July 1963, the company name was changed to reflect its status as a division of **Hawker Siddeley Aviation Ltd**. For details of Hawker Siddeley activities, see the entry for Bitteswell, which also summarises the flight test work carried out in support of **Armstrong Siddeley Motors Ltd**.

Carbodies, of Holyhead Road, Coventry, were advertising in December 1938 that they 'supply the engine cowling pressings and other details on the Supermarine Spitfire'.

The **Coventry Aviation Co.**, of 34A Earl Street, Coventry, was registered in November 1917 for the manufacture of 'Metal aeroplane and other parts'. The company name was changed to **Coventry Aviation Co. Ltd** in September 1918, but nothing else is known.

The **Coventry Ordnance Works Ltd** was registered on 2 June 1905, and from 1906 also included **Fairfield Shipbuilding & Engineering Ltd** at Govan. The company took over **Warwick Wright Ltd** in late 1911, *Flight* reporting in January 1912 that 'the Howard T. Wright company was being absorbed by the Coventry Ordnance Works'. The Coventry Ordnance Works produced two biplane designs to compete in the 1912 Military Trials. The first of these flew successfully from Brooklands, and was test-flown by T.O.M. Sopwith in May 1912. This aircraft was progressively developed and was reported to be flying at

---

THE COVENTRY ORDNANCE WORKS, LIMITED,
COVENTRY.

MONOPLANES AND BIPLANES

Specially designed for **NAVAL** and **MILITARY SERVICE.**

Manager, Aeroplane Department :—**HOWARD T. WRIGHT.**

Monoplanes and biplanes advertised by The Coventry Ordnance Works, 1912.

This BE12, which was built by the Coventry Ordnance Works, shows clearly the single-seater configuration that distinguishes the type from the BE2 series. (Derek James)

Brooklands throughout 1913. The second machine appeared at the Military Trials at Larkhill, but (to quote R. Dallas Brett) 'took no part in the proceedings [...] by reason of a serious defect in the magneto drive of its Chenu engine'.

After this initial activity, the company then started experimental aircraft construction under W.O. Manning, using a small part of their complex between Red Lane and Midland Road, Coventry (currently a rather run-down area to be found off Ordnance Road, just to the north of the Coventry Canal). The Coventry Ordnance Works Ltd undertook extensive production during the First World War, including the following:

- BE 2A/B/C: Robertson's *British Military Aircraft Serials 1878-1987* lists eight BE2A and one BE2C as being built by COW. The manufacturers of many BE2 aircraft in this early range of serials are not listed, and COW may, therefore, have built additional examples.
- BE8A: Twenty-one aircraft, serials 2154–2174.
- BE12A: Fifty aircraft.
- RE7: Fifty aircraft.

- RE8: 450 aircraft.
- Sopwith Snipe: At least forty-three from 150 ordered in the batch E6537–E6686, a second contract for 150 being cancelled.

The Coventry Ordnance Works was absorbed into the aircraft activities of the English Electric Co. Ltd in December 1918. This was announced as follows: 'THE ENGLISH ELECTRIC Co. which incorporates the Works of MESSRS. COVENTRY ORDNANCE, DICK KERR and PHOENIX DYNAMO MFG. Co., has consolidated the joint aircraft experience and plant of the three concerns in one large central factory, having exceptional manufacturing and testing facilities' (advertisement in 1919 *Jane's All the World's Aircraft*). The companies were amalgamated in December 1918 with 'Works – Thornbury and Scotstoun, Aircraft Offices – Thornbury Works, Bradford, and Central Offices – Queen's House, Kingsway, London'. The centralisation at Bradford referred to above took place in March 1919.

The Daimler Co. Ltd: The Daimler Motor Co. was established in 1896 at Motor Mills, Sandy Lane, Coventry. Daimler was saved from financial difficulties when it was acquired by Birmingham Small Arms Co. in 1909. A new factory, known as the Radford Works, was opened in 1912.

George Bulman, who was later famous as Hawker's chief test pilot, undertook test-flying for Daimler, this being conducted at Radford. The types built by Daimler were the BE2C (200), BE12/12A/12B (500), RE8 (1,450), and DH10 (about forty-eight aircraft were built from an order for 150). Some 150 of the Daimler-built BE12 were completed as BE12B, with 200hp Hispano Suiza engines being fitted at the Northern Aircraft Repair Depot at Coal Aston, near Sheffield. With its production total approaching 2,200 aircraft, and a single order placed for 850 RE8 (the largest single order of the First World War), Daimler was one of the most important contractors.

This Daimler-built BE2C is one of 200 built by the company, whose main production type was the RE8.
(BAE SYSTEMS plc)

The **Humber Motor Co. Ltd** had its origins in the bicycle industry. Humber began manufacturing Blériot-derived monoplanes initially with their own 30hp three-cylinder radial engines in 1910. The company conducted manufacturing operations at Coventry, with flying at Brooklands. Humber made every component of the aircraft including the propellers in their own factory. As well as a small number of Blériot-derived machines, Humber built a monoplane designed by Hubert Le Blon, which featured a slim tapered tubular fuselage, which the pilot sat *on* (in horse-riding style), rather than *in*. This machine, which was displayed at Olympia in 1910, is thought not to have been flown. The company also built a number of biplanes of 'Boxkite', or 'Sommer-type', configuration.

In August 1912, Humber announced that they were giving up aircraft manufacture, offering for auction on 4 September eight Blériot monoplanes, one Humber-built Blériot and three Humber-built Sommer biplanes, an additional Sommer and a Humber Lovelace monoplane with 28hp engine, together with engines, propellers and parts.

Humber later restarted aircraft construction to support the First World War effort. A photograph in *The Aeroplane*, during April 1918, shows wing manufacture in full flow. The main aircraft production during the First World War was of the Avro 504, production including the 504A, J and K models. Orders totalled 850 aircraft, of which 664 were delivered. Humber also built aircraft engines, including the notorious ABC Dragonfly. An important contribution made by the company was the development of the powerful Bentley BR1 rotary.

The Humber factory at Folly Lane (later renamed Humber Road), Stoke, Coventry covered 22.5 acres and, when it was opened in 1908, was the largest car factory in England until Ford opened their Trafford Park factory in 1911. Humber was absorbed into the Rootes Group in 1931. The Stoke factory continued in use for many years as Rootes passed on to Chrysler and Peugeot-Talbot. This huge factory continues in use today, the frontage of some of its buildings being emblazoned 'Humber Hillman'.

Lea Francis Engineering Ltd of Much Park Street, Coventry, manufactured Short Stirling sheet-metal components during the Second World War.

Rudge-Whitworth Ltd was originally a supplier of wheels for the motor industry and is also famous for both cycles and motorcycles. *The Aeroplane* reported that Rudge-Whitworth 'have since the outbreak of the War, laid down a very complete plant for the production of parts of aeroplanes'. At this time, the company was advertising its ability to supply 'metal fittings for BE2C'.

In 1919 the company slogan was 'Britain's Best Bicycle'. The war record was, however, not forgotten:

> *Aeronautical Department: Our four years experience of Government work building complete components. Specialists in Planes, Tails, Fins, Rudders, Skids, Undercarriages, Ailerons, Elevators, Airship cars, Radiator shutters, Tie-rods, Metal fittings, Metal spars, Ball bearings. Rudge-Whitworth detachable wire wheels are fitted to all high-grade makes of cars and aeroplanes.*

The **Standard Motor Co. Ltd** produced aircraft during both the First and Second World War. An early advertising slogan was 'Makers of Aeroplanes'. The company was a pioneer of 'standardised' production in the UK car industry, this innovation giving rise to the company name Standard Motor Co. Ltd. Initially construction was at Cash's Lane, Coventry.

The main types built (totalling nearly 3,400 aircraft) were as follows:

- Bristol Fighter: At least seventy-four.
- BE12: Fifty at Cash's Lane.
- RE8: 600 at Canley.

The Standard Motor Co. Ltd built aircraft in both world wars. In the First World War, their contribution included at least 850 Sopwith Pup, together with the RE8, Bristol Fighter and BE12. This Pup displays a particularly striking colour scheme. (Terry C. Treadwell and Alan C. Wood)

- Sopwith Pup: At least 850. The first Sopwith Pup built by The Standard Motor Co. Ltd carried serial A626.

And in the Second World War:

- Airspeed Oxford: 750.
- De Havilland Mosquito: 1,066.

During the First World War, a new factory was commissioned at Canley, near Coventry for aircraft production. This factory was used for Oxford and Mosquito manufacture during the Second World War. The company also produced Beaufighter components. Aircraft built during the Second World War were erected, test-flown and delivered from Ansty (Warwickshire). The Canley site ultimately became a Rover factory, but by 1997 the entire ninety-five-acre site was being redeveloped as Coventry Business Park. The small Cash's Lane factory remained in use as an industrial unit.

Dunstall Park (Wolverhampton)

The racecourse at Dunstall Park was the scene of much early flying including the third British flying meeting held in June 1910. A series of wooden hangars were built on the canal side of the racecourse.

The 1910 Dunstall Park meeting included most of the noteworthy pilots of the day, including C.S. Rolls, Cecil Grace, C. Grahame-White, Alec Ogilvie, James Radley, Graham Gilmour, and H.J.D. Astley, among others. Dunstall Park was the first aerodrome to be used by the Midland Aero Club who abandoned it in favour of Castle Bromwich in 1912.

The **Harthill** Monoplane was a Demoiselle-inspired monoplane constructed in Wolverhampton by Edgar Harthill for a Dr Hands. It was tested (unsuccessfully) at Dunstall Park in 1910.

Mann Monoplane: It is reported in *British Aircraft Before the Great War* that a monoplane built by G.B. Mann of Wolverhampton was tested unsuccessfully at Dunstall Park in September

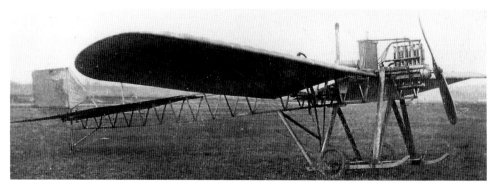

The Star monoplane was built in Wolverhampton by the car manufacturer Star Engineering Co. and was tested at Dunstall Park and at Brooklands. (Alec Brew)

1910. The aircraft structure was constructed of steel tubing, but, despite its practical appearance, there is no record of it having flown successfully.

Star Engineering Co., Frederick Street, Wolverhampton (1910), built a monoplane designed by Granville Bradshaw, and a Farman-style biplane. These aircraft were tested at Dunstall Park, but are not believed to have been successful. To quote Dallas Brett: 'The Midland Aero Club had established an aerodrome at Dunstall Park where several unorthodox aircraft were being put through their paces. They included [...] the Star monoplane made by the Star Car Co. of Wolverhampton [...] None of these craft was very successful.' Star had started life as a cycle manufacturer – the Star Cycle Co. Ltd, adding cars in 1898, being renamed the Star Motor Co. Ltd, which company finally closed in the 1930s.

The 1910 Star monoplane is described as being based on the Antoinette design, and featured a triangular section fuselage. Later, it was modified to include rounded wing tips and a more conventional tail replacing the narrow triangular (Antoinette-inspired) surfaces originally used. It remained only modestly successful, but was flown at both Dunstall Park, and at Brooklands (in December 1910 and January 1911).

Star was, after Sunbeam, the most important vehicle manufacturer in Wolverhampton prior to the First World War. Star also built twelve Renault V8 engines from a 1918 order for 400, at the end of the First World War.

Sunbeam Motor Co. Ltd: Dunstall Park was used for test-flying the aircraft built by Sunbeam Motor Co. Ltd during the First World War.

Wright Forge & Engineering Co. Ltd, Tipton, Staffordshire, produced a School biplane described in *Flight* in June 1917. This was a very neat design, being a tandem two-seat, single-bay biplane powered by a 45hp Anzani radial. The aircraft had no fixed fin and was otherwise distinguished by the front cockpit being located ahead of the centre section struts, and by the fuselage being fully ply-covered for extra strength. The aircraft was designed by Mr W. Westwood, and test-flown at Dunstall Park by René Desoutter. The aircraft was advertised for sale in August 1917 and April 1920. Note: Joseph Wright and Co. ran a forge at Tipton; Howard T. Wright, the pioneer constructor and designer, was Joseph Wright's son.

Walsall

Helliwells Ltd were based at Walsall Municipal Airport, Bosty Lane, Aldridge. The airport, which was a fairly confined field on a sloping site, came into use from around 1933.

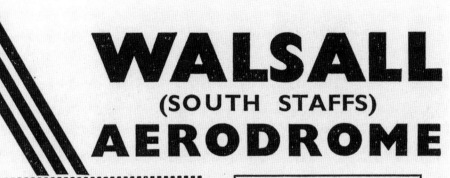

Walsall Aerodrome.

Helliwells Ltd of Walsall made an important contribution during the Second World War.

Helliwells Ltd was an engineering company, which was founded at Fountain Street, Dudley, in 1889 manufacturing fire irons and fireguards and the like. From 1935 the company took up aircraft work and an impressive factory building was erected at Walsall Airport, these works being opened in October 1938. During the pre-war expansion period the company had contracts for components (mainly fuel and oil tanks and windscreen frames) for a diverse range of types including the Hart, Hurricane, Blenheim, Wellesley, Gladiator, Whitley and Anson. Helliwells Ltd was a UK sister design authority for the Harvard and Boston during the Second World War; many of these aircraft being assembled, modified, repaired and test-flown here, and from Elmdon. Other work included Hurricane repairs and the manufacture of Wellington bomb beams.

After the war, Helliwells also refurbished a number of Seafire and Harvard aircraft. Plans were announced in 1947 for Helliwells Ltd to produce the Globe Swift as the Helliwell Globe; these came to nothing, however. In 1953, the company was describing its business as 'repair, overhaul and modification of service and civil aircraft'. The last aircraft was overhauled in 1956, following which the airfield closed.

Whitley Abbey (Coventry)

This site, one mile to the north of the later factory and test airfield at Baginton, was for many years the main production facility of **Sir W.G. Armstrong Whitworth Aircraft Ltd**, and was purchased by John Siddeley in late 1923.

The main aircraft types flown at Whitley included:

A view of Whitley Abbey in 1928. Flight operations were later transferred to Baginton and Bitteswell.
(Ray Williams archive)

A line of Gloster-built Siskin IIIA fighters. Contract production of this type played a role in migrating metal construction techniques across the aircraft industry. (Ken Ellis collection)

The Atlas was a very successful Army Co-operation machine that was also used for training. This is a civilian-registered Atlas Trainer, seen here at Whitley Abbey, where it was built in September 1930. (Ray Williams archive)

- Siskin II: G-EBUU, G-EBHY in August 1922.
- Awana: J6897 in 1923 – a large twin-engine transport biplane with a wingspan of more than 100ft.
- Siskin III: Prototype J6853 first flew on 7 May 1923.
- Siskin IIIA: The main production version – J7001 – first flew on 21 October 1925.
- Atlas: Unglamorous but highly successful, the Atlas was first flown at Whitley on 10 May 1925 (G-EBLK, later J8765). The Atlas served in the unfashionable roles of Army co-operation and training, and was also exported to Canada, Greece, Japan, and Kwangsi Province. 478 were built, 175 as dual-control trainers (some sources give the total as 486, also 446).

Construction of the Armstrong Whitworth Argosy airliner underway at Whitley Abbey. (BAE SYSTEMS plc via Ray Williams)

THE AW. XV. ATALANTA

The Astraea, an Imperial Airways Liner of the Atalanta class, in front of the hanger at Dum-Dum, Calcutta Airport.

G-ABTL

A 5 78.

SIR W. G. ARMSTRONG WHITWORTH AIRCRAFT LIMITED., WHITLEY, COVENTRY, ENGLAND

An Atlanta in service with Imperial Airways photographed at Dum-Dum Airport, Calcutta. (BAE SYSTEMS plc)

The Atalanta was a great step forward in aerodynamic efficiency with its smooth lines and cantilever monoplane wing, compared with the utilitarian lines of the three-engine biplane Argosy, which had flown only six years earlier. (Ray Williams archive)

- Argosy three-engined biplane airliner, seven of which were built; see additional comments below.
- Armstrong Whitworth built a total of 456 Hawker Hart and Hart Trainer under contract.
- A.W.XV Atalanta: The exceptionally clean Armstrong Whitworth A.W.XV Atalanta four-engine monoplane airliner G-ABPI first flew at Whitley on 6 June 1932; eight were built.
- A.W.38 Whitley bomber, see comments below.

Lesser-known prototypes of the 1920s and '30s that were flown here included:

- Wolf: Single example, J6921, competed with the Hawker Duiker and Short Springbok against Specification 8/22, for an Army co-operation machine. The Wolf was an unattractive biplane, with its fuselage mid-set between its wings.
- A.W.XIV Starling: First flown 19 May 1927.
- A.W.XVI: Total of twenty built including prototypes, seventeen being exported to Kwangsi province.
- A.W. XVII Aries: A Warren-strutted biplane intended to replace the Atlas. Single example J9037, first flown 5 March 1930.
- The Swordfish-like A.W.19.
- A.W.23 bomber transport (a slab-sided pantechnicon of an aircraft): The A.W.23 K3585 was first flown on 4 June 1935 and was later used (as G-AFRX) for air-to-air refuelling trials by Flight Refuelling Ltd.

J8027 is the A.W.XIV Starling 1, photographed at Whitley Abbey, where it made its first flight in May 1927. This aircraft was exhibited at Olympia in 1929 with registration G-AAHC. (Ray Williams archive)

An Armstrong Whitworth advertisement to illustrate the most important of the types to be built at Whitley Abbey: the A.W.38 Whitley bomber. (BAE SYSTEMS plc)

- A.W.29 day bomber: An unsuccessful competitor to the Fairey Battle.
- A.W.35 Scimitar: Two private-venture prototypes and four aircraft exported to Norway.

One of Armstrong Whitworth's best-known early products, the Argosy was the largest British airliner of its time. The prototype G-EBLF first flew on 16 March 1926. The Argosy fleet gave Imperial Airways many years of service on the London–Paris route, and later to more far-flung destinations.

By April 1930, the Argosy had a solid and safe reputation, as is reflected in the following advertisement:

> *Over 1,000,000 miles. In just over four years, seven Argosies in the European Fleet of Imperial Airways Ltd have flown 1,023,075 miles in approximately 11,296 hours. They have carried over 80,000 passengers; they have crossed the Channel approximately 4,200 times. The Argosies are the safest, best paying and most easily maintained airliners in existence.*

The name Argosy was resurrected for Armstrong Whitworth's last design, the Argosy military and civil freighter, which flew for the first time in 1959 at Bitteswell.

Perhaps most notable of the Whitley products was the Armstrong Whitworth Whitley bomber, whose prototype, K4586, first flew here on 17 March 1936. A total of 1,814 Whitley were built, the most important version being the Mk V, 1,466 of which were built.

The Armstrong Whitworth Flying School was established at Whitley, becoming **Air Service Training Ltd** (AST) in February 1931, before moving to Hamble, Hampshire in April of the same year.

N1349 is a Whitley V, the most important version of the Whitley, 1,466 being built. (Ken Ellis collection)

Although Sir W.G. Armstrong Whitworth Aircraft Ltd subsequently centred their aircraft assembly and test activities at Baginton (Warwickshire) and Bitteswell (Leicestershire), the Whitley site continued in use into the 1950s (being used at that time for missile development work). The Jaguar Engineering Centre now occupies the Whitley site.

Wolverhampton

Wolverhampton Municipal Airport at Pendeford opened on 25 June 1938 and was used as the production airfield of **Boulton Paul Aircraft Ltd.** This company was formed in 1934 at Norwich to take over the Aircraft Department of **Boulton & Paul Ltd**. From 1961, the company was styled **Dowty Boulton Paul Ltd**, and from 1991 **Dowty Aerospace**. The company now forms part of Smiths Group.

In August 1936 Boulton Paul Aircraft Ltd moved to Pendeford, Wobaston Rd, Wolverhampton. Initial production at Wolverhampton consisted of Hawker Demon aircraft, Saro London wings, Fairey Seafox tails, and all of the Blackburn-designed Roc aircraft (136), the first of which, L3057, flew on 23 December 1938. At the time of their move to Wolverhampton, Boulton Paul Aircraft were in fact part way through their production of 106 Hawker Demon aircraft, fifty-nine of which were completed at Norwich, and forty-seven at Wolverhampton. In September 1936, the company was advertising from its new location: 'Boulton Paul Aircraft Ltd, Wolverhampton. Designers and Manufacturers of Military and Civil Aircraft.' The telegraphic address was 'Aircraft, Wolverhampton'.

Boulton Paul's most notable design was the Defiant, which served as a night fighter and target tug. A total of 1,062 were built (some sources state 1,061). The Defiant prototype K8310 first flew at Pendeford on 11 August 1937. Following on from the Defiant, Bolton Paul became a major producer of the Fairey Barracuda, producing 692 aircraft, the first flying in August 1943. Boulton Paul converted 270 Vickers Wellington aircraft to T.10 navigation trainer configuration. The company also built the components of the first prototype Hawker Fury X VB857, this aircraft then being assembled by Hawker. Important wartime activity included gun turret manufacture for many British and American types in RAF service.

In addition to the above, the company was nominated a sister firm for support and modification to the US Havoc, Boston and Harvard aircraft. These types were normally

Boulton Paul Aircraft Ltd were responsible for production of the Blackburn Roc, building 136 aircraft in a single batch. (BAE SYSTEMS plc)

The Boulton Paul Defiant turret fighter was relegated to night fighting after a short period of day operations. (via Author)

Boulton Paul Aircraft Ltd were a major manufacturer of the Fairey Barracuda, building 692 of these imposing aircraft. (Boulton Paul Association)

flight-tested at RAF Perton due to the unsuitable grass surface at Pendeford. This work was shared with Helliwells Ltd. at Walsall.

Post-war production included the Balliol trainer of which 229 were built (thirty by Blackburn at Brough), and two experimental delta designs, the P.111 and the P.120. The Balliol first flew on 30 May 1947, the prototype VL892 being initially powered by a Bristol Mercury. The first Mamba-powered aircraft VL917 flew on 24 March 1948. All production aircraft were powered by the Rolls-Royce Merlin 35 engine. A total of two prototypes, seventeen pre-production and 165 production aircraft (Balliol T. Mk 2) were built, nine of these being supplied to the Royal Ceylon Air Force. The Royal Navy received thirty Sea Balliol T. Mk 21.

The P.111 VT935 first flew on 6 October 1950, and was followed on 6 August 1952 by P.120 VT951. The brief flying career of the P.120 was centred on Boscombe Down, where the aircraft crashed on 29 August 1952 after less than a month of flying. Sub-contract production during the 1950s included wings for the Supermarine Swift.

Jet aircraft testing was carried out at Seighford, near Stafford, mainly on the development of modifications to the Canberra (camera installation on PR.3/7 variants, conversion of B.2 to T.11 with conical radar nose, four cannon pack for the B(I). Mk 8, and so on). Radar signature reduction trials featured both the Balliol and Canberra, and there was additional work in 1961 to convert the Lightning F.1 to the F.3.

The experimental Tay Viscount incorporated the world's first electrically-signalled flight controls for which Boulton Paul was responsible. The company closed its flight test department in 1965. During the entire aircraft manufacturing life of the company, 4,826 aircraft were built, of which 1,341 were of its own design. 2,198 aircraft were built at Wolverhampton.

Guy Motors, and **Clyno Cars**, both of Wolverhampton built small numbers (a total of six) of ABC engines from large contracts (a total of 1,112), cancelled at the end of the First World War.

Marston Ltd, of Paul Street, Wolverhampton, is listed in *The Aviation Pocket-Book of 1919-20* as an aircraft manufacturer, but its main product is believed to have been aircraft radiators. This work continued (as Marston Radiators Ltd) during the Second World War. In 1954, the company was trading as Marston Excelsior Ltd, with head office at Fordhouses, Wolverhampton, and specialised in 'design and manufacture of all types of heat exchangers; flexible fuel and oil tanks for aircraft; reinforced laminated plastics for radar housings; the machining and assembly of aircraft hydraulic and other components; specialists in metal fabrications for the aircraft industry' .

Balliol G-ANSF was used by Boulton Paul Aircraft Ltd as a company demonstration aircraft.
(Boulton Paul Aircraft Ltd via Ken Ellis)

Wolverhampton Aviation Ltd assembled a number of Gemini 3A aircraft, of which G-AMME was the last, from parts of acquired following the winding up of Miles Aircraft Ltd. (NA3T Transport Archive)

Redwing Aircraft Co. Ltd set up a company in Wolverhampton to manufacture Defiant fuselages under sub-contract, using the buildings of a disused iron foundry. The company also operated at Croydon and nearby Thornton Heath, and at Colchester.

Sunbeam Motor Co. Ltd, Morefield Works, Upper Villiers Street., Wolverhampton. Sunbeam Motor Co. Ltd had its origins in the cycle industry, but by 1913 Sunbeam were Britain's third largest car manufacturer. During the First World War, they produced large numbers of aircraft engines under the name Sunbeam-Coatalen (Crusader, Mohawk, Gurkha, Zulu, Cossack, Afridi, Maori, Manitou, Viking, Nubian, Arab, Dyak, Matabele, Sikh), and a range of aircraft types. The most important engines were the Arab (production of which was also sub-contracted to Austin, Lanchester, Napier, and Willys Overland) and the Maori.

Sunbeam built twenty Short 827, fifteen Short Bomber, fifty Short 320, a single Sunbeam Bomber N515, sixty Avro 504B, and at least 398 Avro 504J/K (a total of 543 aircraft). During this period, Sunbeam had so much aeronautical production that car manufacture had to be transferred to The Rover Company Ltd in Coventry.

Wolverhampton Aviation Ltd was run by the famous racing pilot Ron Paine and assembled five Gemini 3A aircraft between 1950 and 1952 at Wolverhampton Airport (Pendeford), using components originally manufactured at Woodley. The company also converted Gemini 3A G-ALCS to Gemini 3C configuration in July 1957 and converted a number of ex-RAF Messenger aircraft for civil use.

Mr Paine purchased a number of Miles aircraft, following the collapse of Miles Aircraft in 1948. These included the Miles Hawk Speed Six G-ADGP, together with unassembled Gemini components from Woodley and Messenger components from Belfast.

The airfield at Pendeford has now disappeared under housing development, the Council having voted to close the airfield at the end of 1970.

Bibliography

50 Golden Years of Achievement, Hamble 1936-1986 (British Aerospace, 1986)

75 Years of Aviation in Kingston, 1913-1988 (British Aerospace, 1988)

Adventure with Fate, Harald Penrose, Airlife (1984)

The Aeroplane Directory of British Aviation, Staff of *The Aeroplane* (Temple Press Ltd, 1953 edition)

The Aerospace Chronology, Michael J.H. Taylor (Tri-Service Press, 1989)

Aircraft Made in Lincoln, John Walls and Charles Parker (Society of Lincolnshire History & Archaeology, 2000)

Aircraft of the Fighting Powers, Volume 1-5, Edited: D.A. Russell, Compiled: H.J. Cooper, Owen Thetford (Harborough Publishing, 1940–1944)

Aircraft of the Fighting Powers, Volume 6, Edited: D.A. Russell, Compiled: Owen Thetford, C.B. Maycock (Harborough Publishing, 1945)

Aircraft of the Fighting Powers, Volume 7, Edited: D.A. Russell, Compiled: Owen Thetford, E.J. Riding (Harborough Publishing, 1946)

Aircraft of the RAF, a pictorial record 1918-1978, Paul Ellis (Macdonald & Jane's, 1978)

The Aircraft of the World, William Green, and Gerard Pollinger (Macdonald, 1953)

The Aircraft of the World, William Green and Gerard Pollinger (Macdonald, 1955)

The Aircraft of the World, William Green (Macdonald, 1965)

Airlife's General Aviation, R.W. Simpson (Airlife, 1991)

Armstrong Whitworth Aircraft Since 1913, Oliver Tapper (Putnam, 1973)

Auster Aircraft –Auster Production List, N.H. Ellison and R.O. Macdemitria (AIR-BRITAIN, Second Edition, February 1966)

Aviation Archaeology, Bruce Robertson (Patrick Stephens Ltd, second edition 1983)

Aviation in Birmingham, Geoffrey Negus and Tommy Staddon (Midland Counties Publications 1984)

Aviation in Leicestershire and Rutland, Roy Bonser (Midland Publishing, 2001)

Aviation in Manchester, B.R. Robinson (Royal Aeronautical Society, Manchester Branch, 1977)

Aviation Landmarks, Jean Gardner (Battle of Britain Prints International 1990)

The Aviation Pocket-Book 1919-1920, R. Borlase-Matthews (Crosby, Lockwood & Son, seventh edition, 1919)

Avro (Archive Photographs series), Harry Holmes (Chalford Publishing, 1996)

Avro Aircraft since 1908, A.J. Jackson (Putnam, 1965)

AVRO The History of an Aircraft Company, Harry Holmes (Airlife, 1994)

Balloons to Buccaneers - Yorkshire's role in aviation since 1785, Brian Catchpole (Maxiprint, 1994)

The Blackburn Story 1909-1959, Blackburn Aircraft Ltd, 1960

Boulton Paul Aircraft (Archive Photographs series), Boulton Paul Association (Chalford Publishing, 1996)

Brassey's World Aircraft & Systems Directory, Michael Taylor (Brassey's (UK) Ltd, 1996)

Bristol Aircraft since 1910, C.H. Barnes (Putnam, 1964)

Bristol An Aircraft Album, James D. Oughton (Ian Allan 1973)

'Britain's Air Strength', *The Air Defence of Great Britain,* Lt Cdr R. Fletcher, MP (Penguin, October 1938)

Britain's Motor Industry – The first hundred years, Nick Georgano, Nick Baldwin, Anders Clausager, Jonathan Wood (G.T. Foulis & Co., 1995)

British Aeroplanes, 1914-1918, J.M. Bruce (Putnam, 1962)

British Aerospace – The Facts, BAe Corporate Communications (British Aerospace, 1992 and 1996)

British Aircraft at War 1939-45, Gordon Swanborough (HPC Publishing, 1997)

British Aircraft Before The Great War, Michael H. Goodall and Albert E. Tagg (Schiffer Publishing Ltd, 2001)

British Aircraft Manufacturers since 1908, Günter Endres (Ian Allan Publishing, 1995)

British Aircraft of World War II, David Mondey (Chancellor Press 1994 edition)

British Aircraft, 1809-1914, Peter Lewis (Putnam, 1962)

British Aviation – Ominous Skies, Harald Penrose (HMSO, 1980)

British Aviation – The Adventuring Years, Harald Penrose (Putnam, 1973)

British Aviation – The Pioneer Years, Harald Penrose (Cassell Ltd, revised edition 1980)

British Aviation – Widening Horizons, Harald Penrose (HMSO, 1979)

The British Bomber since 1914, F.K. Mason (Putnam, 1994)

British Civil Aircraft since 1919, A.J. Jackson (Putnam, second edition, Vol. 1 1973, Vol. 2 1973, Vol. 3 1974)

British Commercial Aircraft – sixty years in pictures, Paul Ellis (Jane's Publishing, 1980)

The British Fighter since 1912, F.K. Mason (Putnam, 1992)

British Flight Testing: Martlesham Heath 1920-1939, Tim Mason (Putnam, 1993)

British Floatplanes, G.R. Duval (D. Bradford Barton, 1976)

British Homebuilt Aircraft since 1920, Ken Ellis (Merseyside Aviation Society, second edition, 1979)

British Light Aeroplanes – Their Evolution, Development and Perfection 1920 – 1940, Arthur W.J.G. Ord-Hume (GMS Enterprises, 2000)

British Military Aircraft Serials 1878-1987, Bruce Robertson (Midland Counties Publications, 1987)

British Prototype Aircraft, Ray Sturtivant (The Promotional Reprint Co. Ltd, 1995)

British Racing and Record Breaking Aircraft, Peter Lewis (Putnam, 1970)

Brush Aircraft production at Loughborough, A.P. Jarram (Midland Counties Publications, 1978)

Cobham – The Flying Years, Colin Cruddas (Archive Photograph series, Chalford Publishing 1997)

In Cobham's Company – Sixty Years of Flight Refuelling Ltd, Colin Cruddas (Cobham plc 1994)

The Cold War Years – Flight Testing at Boscombe Down 1945-1975, Tim Mason (Hikoki Publications Ltd, 2001)

Dangerous Skies The, A.E. Clouston (Pan Books, 1956)

Discover Aviation Trails, Paul Shaw (Midland Publishing, 1996)

Dizzy Heights – The Story of Lancashire's First Flying Men, Chris Aspin (Helmshore Local History Society, 1988)

English Electric Aircraft and their Predecessors, S. Ransom and R. Fairclough (Putnam, 1987)

Fairey Aircraft since 1915, H.A. Taylor (Putnam, 1974)

Fairey Aviation (Archive Photographs series), J.W.R. Taylor (Chalford Publishing, 1997)

Fighters of the Fifties, Bill Gunston (Patrick Stephens Ltd, 1981)

Filton and the Flying Machine (Archive Photographs series), Malcolm Hall (Chalford Publishing 1995)

The First Croydon Airport 1915-1928, Douglas Cluett, (editor), Bob Learmonth and Joanna Nash (Sutton Libraries and Arts Services, 1977)

First Through the Clouds, F. Warren Merriam (B.T. Batsford Ltd, 1954)

The Flight of the Mew Gull, Alex Henshaw (John Murray, 1980)

Flying Corps Headquarters 1914-1918, Maurice Baring (Buchan & Enright Ltd (reprint, 1985)

The Flying Scots – A century of aviation in Scotland, Jack Webster (The Glasgow Royal Concert Hall, 1994)

Forever Farnborough – Flying the Limits 1904-1996, P.J. Cooper (Hikoki Publications, 1996)

The Forgotten Pilots, Lettice Curtis (Nelson Saunders, third edition, 1985)

Forty Years of the Spitfire – Proceedings of the Mitchell Memorial Symposium, R.A. East and I.C. Cheeseman (Royal Aeronautical Society, Southampton Branch, 1976)

From Spitfire to Eurofighter, Roy Boot (Airlife, 1990)

Gloucestershire Aviation – A History, Ken Wixey (Alan Sutton, 1995)

Handley Page, Alan Dowsett (Tempus Publishing, Images of Aviation Series, 1999)

Hawker – A biography of Harry Hawker, L.K. Blackmore (Airlife, 1993)

Hawker Aircraft since 1920, F.K. Mason (Putnam, 1961)

Helicopters and Autogyros of the World, Paul Lambermont and Anthony Pirie (Cassell, 1958)

Hendon Aerodrome – A History, David Oliver (Airlife, 1994)

The History of Black Country Aviation, Alec Brew (Alan Sutton, 1993)

History of British Aviation 1908-1914, R. Dallas Brett (Air Research Publications & Kristall Productions. Eightieth Anniversary Edition 1988)

A History of the Eastbourne Aviation Company 1911 – 1924, Lou McMahon & Michael Partridge (Eastbourne Local History Society, 2000)

I Kept No Diary, Air Cdre F.R. Banks (Airlife, 1978)

Industry and Air Power. The Expansion of British Aircraft Production, 1935-1941, Sebastian Ritchie (Frank Cass, 1997)

The Jet Aircraft of the World , William Green and Roy Cross (Macdonald, 1955)

Knights of the Air, Peter King (Constable & Co. Ltd, 1989)

Lend-Lease Aircraft of World War II, Arthur Pearcy (Motorbooks International, 1996)

Leysdown – the Cradle of Flight, Brian Slade (Santa–Maria Publications, 1990)

Lion Rampant and Winged, Alan Robertson (Alan Robertson, 1986)

Mach One, Mike Lithgow (Allan Wingate, 1954)

The Magic of a Name, Harold Nockholds (G.T. Foulis & Co. Ltd 1949)

The Marshall Story, Sir Arthur Marshall (Patrick Stephens Ltd, 1994)

Men with Wings, Wg Cdr H.P. 'Sandy' Powell (Allan Wingate, 1957)

More Tails of the Fifties, Editor: Peter G. Campbell (Cirrus Associates (SW), 1998)

Not much of an Engineer, Sir Stanley Hooker (Airlife, 1984)

Parnall's Aircraft, Ken Wixey (Tempus Publishing, Images of England Series, 1998)

Peaceful Fields Volume 1, The South, J.F. Hamlin (GMS Enterprises, 1996)

Plane Speaking, Bill Gunston (Patrick Stephens Ltd, 1991)

Per Ardua – The Rise of British Air Power 1911-1939, Hilary St George Saunders (Oxford University Press, 1944)

Proud Heritage - A Pictorial History of British Aerospace Aircraft, Phil Coulson (Royal Air Force Benevolent Fund, 1995)

Pure Luck - The Authorized Biography of Sir Thomas Sopwith 1888-1989, Alan Bramson (Patrick Stephens Ltd, 1990)

The Quick and The Dead, W.A. Waterton (Frederick Muller Ltd, 1956)

The Redwing Story, John Lane (Mrs Phyllis Lane, 1992)

The Royal Flying Corps, Terry C. Treadwell and Alan C. Wood (Images of Aviation series, Tempus Publishing Ltd, 2000)

The Royal Naval Air Service, Terry C. Treadwell and Alan C. Wood (Images of Aviation series, Tempus Publishing Ltd, 1999)

Schneider Trophy The, David Mondey (Robert Hale, 1975)

Sent Flying, A.J. 'Bill' Pegg (Macdonald, 1959)

Shoreham Airport, Sussex, T.M.A. Webb and Dennis L.Bird (Cirrus Associates (SW), 1996)

Shorts Aircraft since 1900, C.H. Barnes (Putnam, 1989)

Sigh for a Merlin, Alex Henshaw, Crécy Publishing, 1999 reprint

Slide Rule, Nevil Shute (Readers Union, 1956)

Sopwith – The Man and His Aircraft, Bruce Robertson (Air Review Ltd, 1970)

The Speed Seekers, Thomas G. Foxworth (Macdonald and Jane's, 1975)

The Spider Web, Sqn Ldr T.D. Hallam (Arms & Armour Press (reprint), 1979)

Spirit of Hamble – Folland Aircraft, Derek N. James (Tempus Publishing, 2000)

Spitfire - A Test Pilot's Story, J.K. Quill (John Murray, 1983)

The Spitfire Story, Alfred Price (Arms & Armour Press, second edition, 1995)

Staffordshire and Black Country Airfields (Archive Photographs series), Alec Brew (Chalford Publishing 1997)

Stirling Wings - The Short Stirling goes to War, Jonathan Falconer (Budding Books, 1995)

The Story of Acton Aerodrome and the Alliance Factory (London Borough of Ealing Library Service, second edition, 1978 with Addenda and Corrigenda)

The Story of the British Light Aeroplane, Terence Boughton (John Murray, 1963)

Supermarine (Archive Photographs series), Norman Barfield (Chalford Publishing, 1996)

Supermarine Spitfire - 40 Years On, G.N.M. Gingell (Royal Aeronautical Society, Southampton Branch, 1976)

Sywell – The Story of an English Aerodrome 1928-1978, Christopher Paul (Sywell Aerodrome Ltd, 1978)

Tails of the Fifties, Editor: Peter G. Campbell (Cirrus Associates (SW), 1997)

Test Pilot, Nevil Duke (Allan Wingate, 1953)

Test Pilots - The story of British Test Flying 1903-1984, Don Middleton (Willow Books, 1985)

Testing Time, Constance Babington Smith (Cassell & Co Ltd, 1961)

That Nothing Failed Them, Air Cdre A.H. Wheeler (G.T. Foulis & Co. Ltd, 1963)

Three Centuries to Concorde, Charles Burnet (Mechanical Engineering Publications Ltd, 1979)

A Time to Fly, Sir Alan Cobham (Shepheard-Walwyn, 1978)

Ultralights - The Early British Classics, Richard Riding (Patrick Stephens Ltd, 1987)

Vapour Trails, Mike Lithgow (Allan Wingate, 1956)

Vickers Aircraft since 1908, C.F. Andrews, E.B. Morgan (Putnam, second edition, 1988)

War in the Air, Edward Smithies (Penguin, 1992)

Westland 50, J.W.R. Taylor and Maurice F. Allward (Ian Allan, 1965)

Westland Aircraft since 1919, D.N. James (Putnam, 1991)

Wings over Woodley – The Story of Miles Aircraft and the Adwest Group, Julian C. Temple, (Aston Publications, 1987)

World Encyclopaedia of Aircraft Manufacturers, Bill Gunston (Patrick Stephens Ltd, 1993)

Magazines and other publications:

Flight: Numerous editions of 'The First Aero Weekly in the World - A Journal Devoted to the Interests, Practice and Progress of Aerial Locomotion and Transport. Official Organ of The Royal Aero Club of the United Kingdom'.

The Aeroplane: Numerous editions, Temple Press Ltd, Editors C.G. Grey and Thurstan James

Aeroplane Monthly: Numerous editions, IPC Magazines Ltd.

The Aeroplane Spotter July 1941 – December 1945, Temple Press Ltd

Jane's All the Worlds Aircraft: various editions from 1909 to date, published by Samson Low, Jane's Information Group, and (reprints) David & Charles Ltd, Collins & Jane's.

Popular Flying: The Magazine of the Popular Flying Association

Royal Air Force Flying Review: 1954-55, 1957-58, 1961-62. A Mercury House Publication.

Index

If you are interested in purchasing other books published by Tempus,
or in case you have difficulty finding any Tempus books in your local bookshop,
you can also place orders directly through our website

www.tempus-publishing.com